Inspiring you to
differenc

Character

Building

Edited by Dawn McGruer

Published by

SPECIALISTS IN MARKETING

SPECIALISTS IN MARKETING

First published 2001 by Aurora
Suite 12, First Floor,
Rex Buildings, 17 Alderley Road,
Wilmslow, Cheshire. SK9 1HY

First Edition
ISBN 0-9541403-0-3

Collection copyright ©Dawn McGruer trading as Aurora
2001

Edited by Dawn McGruer
For copyright of contributors see next page.

A CIP catalogue record for this book is available at the
British Library.

Printed and bound by MFP Design & Print, Stretford,
Manchester.

Copyrights

Contents

⌘

Diagnosis

New life, New joy

'Cancer Research Campaign'

⌘

The Cancer Research Campaign founded in 1923 - supports a comprehensive programme of research in institutes, hospitals, universities and medical schools throughout the United Kingdom. The Campaign is the European leader in anti-cancer drug development and their extensive and effective programme of research ensures that new treatments reach patients as quickly as possible

The Campaign contribute through CRC clinical departments to improvements in treatment for adults and children with cancer while research on the causes and development of the disease underpins the design of entirely novel approaches to treatment and prevention. Through research on the genetic and environmental basis of cancer the Campaign aims to identify those at high risk and to examine the possibilities for reducing that risk to prevent cancer. The development of screening programmes for the early detection of the disease is another priority.

The Cancer Research Campaign work to improve the well being of patients through research on the psychological impact of cancer and to improve communication between doctor and patient. The Campaign provide authoritative cancer information and guidelines for general practitioners and promote cancer prevention through education and research.

The Campaign also has a commitment to train the next generation of cancer scientists and doctors.

The Cancer Research Campaign are dedicated to discovering new cancer treatments and cures. The Cancer Research Campaign has already brought hope to many thousands of people. But there is still a huge amount that they can do and they relies on the support and generosity of people to continue the Campaign's vital work.

Key aims are to fund research of the highest quality and to carry out all goals with maximum cost-efficiency!

Statistics

- Finding the causes of cancer will help scientists develop new ways of preventing and treating it. That is why research, backed up by fundraising, is so important and why The Cancer Research Campaign is so committed to work in the laboratories.

- The lifetime risk of developing cancer is more than one in three, so we may all know someone with the disease. But in these days of new technology and scientific advances we may also equally know someone who has had successful treatment and is now living a normal life.

- Breast cancer is now the most common form of cancer in the UK. But advances in treatment means that seven out of ten women now survive. Those statistics used to make far grimmer reading because in the years from 1971-75, just 54 per cent of women survived.

- Cancer is still the commonest cause of deaths from illness in children aged one to fourteen. But despite this, there has been a dramatic improvement in the cure rates of childhood cancer in recent years, thanks to scientific discovery.

- More than 70 per cent of all cancers in children are successfully treated. And for some cancers, including the most common type of leukaemia, the cure rate is more than 90 per cent.

- There are one million people alive in the UK who have received successful cancer treatment. In others words, of the 250,000 new cases of cancer in the UK every year, 100,000 are cured.

- Following the remarkable scientific breakthrough – the mapping of the human genome – there could not be a better time than the present to fund cutting edge research.

Most importantly trends in survival are improving for almost all types of cancer partially due to the help from cancer research organisations and their fundraising for research efforts.

Research cures cancer – research needs money!

Joanna Lavelle
(Regional Director at 'The Cancer Research Campaign')

Character building is a truly inspiring collection of stories of how the writers have faced the challenges they have met in their lives. A diagnosis of cancer is one of the greatest challenges any of us can meet, but thanks to research, more than 100,000 people are treated successfully every year in the United Kingdom. Research really does find the cures for cancer. However, research does cost money. If you would like to know more about the Cancer Research Campaign contact our website www.crc.org.uk or ring our regional office 0161 772 5555.

Thank you for your support

Anyone wishing.to make a donation directly to the Cancer Research Campaign should send their donation to;

The Cancer Research Campaign,
Furness House,
Furness Quay,
Salford Quays,
Manchester.
M2 5XA.

Cheques should be made payable to The Cancer Research Campaign. To make a donation by credit card or for further information please ring freefone 0800 3280038.

Introduction

⌘

This is an important idea and deserves an audience and will help people as well as raising money for a good cause.

All around the world people are dealing with immensely distressing events and may find it difficult to see the light at the end of the tunnel and who may question whether their lives can continue.

This publication tells how you can survive even the most painful experiences and come out at the end a stronger person who is ready to face the world and seize every opportunity and lead life to the full. The other angle that this book focuses on is the joyous experiences that come to us all at some points in our lives and how those events make us more positive characters and how we adapt the way we lead our lives for the better because of these positive experiences.

We have included biographical paragraphs for some of the authors. Those that do not have biographical details maybe because pieces are written by pseudo or anonymous authors or their stories tell their biography.

Comments From
Actor Nickolas Grace

All our lives have been affected in some way by the scourge of cancer. We may have lost friends or family, or know someone who is fighting the disease now. Here is a book to comfort your soul and to make your heart soar. It contains two valuable weapons with which to fight cancer:

Sensitivity and a sense of humour!

These pieces have been written by people who have experienced or witnessed the anguish and the pain of cancer and by people who know that there is a way to get through adversity.

Whatever our own state of health, we need to live everyday to the full. This book will help us on our way, and will help the Cancer Research Campaign to eventually win the battle against cancer.

Believe in the power of positive thought, believe in the work of the Cancer Research Campaign and believe that one-day we shall beat cancer.

Acknowledgements

⌘

I would like to thank everyone who has supported the project at any stage - from the contributing authors to the companies that have assisted with any aspect of the production of the book. Without you the project would not have been possible.

In addition, thank you to my family for believing in the project and my capabilities of making it work. Also, thanks to everyone that I have used as guinea pigs to trial the content and layout ideas of the book.

I am also eternally grateful for the support of Sir Nigel Hawthorne CBE DL, Anthea Turner, Anna Walker, Philip Schofield, Nickolas Grace and Annette Crosby.

Dedications

⌘

I would like to dedicate this book to several people
who unfortunately are no longer with us due to
illness and tragedy.

William Gordon Black McGruer

May Robertson

Irene Stewart

Graham Foden

I would also like to dedicate this book to the authors
(who have their work published in this book) and to
others in the world who have lost their battle against
cancer. I send my deepest sympathy to their friends
and family.

Inspiring you to make a difference!

Character

Building

Every Cloud Has a Silver Lining
John Milton

1

Anthea Turner

⌘

Foreword

The rough draft of this book arrived at my door on one of those miserable days - we all have them. Something doesn't go to plan, a hurtful comment is made, it's raining and as my Mother would say — 'You can't see the wood for the trees'. For these reasons I am personally recommending this book to be treasured. On those down days it will put perspective back into your life and if you're truly dealing with a crisis you'll know you're not alone. Seek comfort in this beautiful gift of words as I did.

Dawn McGruer

⌘

The Reasons Behind 'Character Building'

The question that I have been asked most during this project is — What inspired you to put this publication together?

So I feel I should explain to you where it all started and the reasons behind this book.

I have always wanted to produce a book of sorts but had never really settled on an idea that inspired me or which I believed was worthy of printing.

It was a bank holiday earlier this year and I had just returned from a weekend break in Abersoch with some friends. I had wanted to visit a friend's grave for a few weeks but had procrastinated over actually going. I suddenly decided that now was the time. It was approximately one month after the fifth year anniversary of his death. I wanted to visit a period after the actual anniversary date partly because I believe that this is the family's time to remember.

I drove up to the graveyard and as I walked through the gates I felt very emotional and my pace slowed. I saw a lady near the gates who was returning the watering can. As I passed her I think she realised that I looked a little lost and bewildered, so she approached me and asked what I thought initially was a strange question – Who are you looking for? I replied and she immediately knew the exact spot in which my friend was laid to rest. This was very calming but also disturbed me due to the fact I wondered how she knew – Was she a friend, family member, etc.?

My curiosity got the better of me and I asked, "How do you know where my friend is buried?"

She replied saying "My son is laid to rest next to him". I wished I had not asked that question. I felt a cold rush through my body and my eyes fill.

She reclaimed the watering can and we walked towards the headstone of my friend and that of her son's. As we walked she started to tell me about her son. He was twenty-one when he was tragically killed in a road accident. As she spoke of her son's death she progressed onto telling me about his personality, life, ambitions, girlfriend, friends, etc. My eyes welled up with tears and I was extremely thankful of my sunglasses at this stage.

We arrived at the grave and I started to replace the dead flowers at my friend's grave with my fresh bouquet. I started to laugh and said, "I don't know why I bring flowers because when he was alive I could never imagine him having any association with floral arrangements. So why would he want them now?" She laughed too and said her son was the same. Her son's grave was covered with white and red roses, which signified the colours of his favourite football team. She said it doesn't matter whether somebody ever liked flowers - they should signify your remembrance of that person. She explained the flowers aspect as more of a symbol for that person's family and it shows that others haven't forgotten them and still care, even years after their death.

Her explanation gave my bouquet a sense of purpose and I felt glad that I had brought flowers.

Once I had finished arranging the flowers we continued talking. It was bizarre because I was sharing my feelings with a complete stranger and vice-versa. We talked about the people that we were there to pay our respects to. This lady gave me the perspective of a mother's grief from losing a son and I gave mine of losing a dear friend. We talked about every aspect of our losses and gave comfort to each other.

I explained all the circumstances to her about his death and she gave me answers from a mother's perspective of how I handled things with his family etc. It was like being reassured that I had done all I could for the family in their time of need. She told me that the help I gave would have meant so much to the family. This gave me a tremendous sense of well being.

Once we had discussed many of the aspects of our loss and grief, we were both very emotional and tears were rolling down our faces. Then we both stopped talking and stood silently in front of the respective gravestones. We both turned, said good-bye, thanked each other for the time we had given to share our feelings and then walked away, probably never to see each other again.

As I exited the gates of the graveyard I felt as if a huge weight had been lifted from my shoulders. This is when the British Telecom catchphrase and famous cliché circled in my head – it's good to talk!

I felt very much inspired to live my life to the full as I was lucky enough to still be here and in good health.

Over the next few weeks I told a few select people of my experience and how it had helped me get over my friend's death. As I told my story to my friends and other acquaintances they began to tell me of similar situations. I learnt from talking to more people that talking and writing seemed to be great healers of adversity. They both seemed to give clarity and perspective in difficult times and helped people overcome negative aspects in their lives.

One night in bed as I mulled over these conversations I realised that talking about difficult times, hearing about others (to know you weren't alone) and writing about feelings really were a therapy to overcome adversity because they released emotions that had built up.

This thought process led me into the idea of producing a book that would inspire others to lead life to the full and that would also help them to overcome adversity. I believed that the best way to do this was to compile an anthology by various authors with differing circumstances and perspectives. This anthology of short stories and poems would be about times in their lives that had resulted in changing their view of life in a positive manner.

I went on holiday for a week and ran through the project in more detail in my head. When I returned I wrote down a brief plan and it was at this point I decided that a secondary purpose of the book would be to raise some money for a charity. I decided that I could fund the project and donate a portion of the cover price that would increase as more copies were sold. I wanted the donations to go to a cancer charity so the 'Cancer Research Campaign' sprung to mind. My reasons for a cancer charity were mainly due to the fact that there are few people in the world that haven't been touched by cancer in some way in their lives and because I have also had personal experiences with cancer in my family.

I approached the charity and they believed it to be a good idea and we progressed into forming a contract. I then advertised for authors and received a tremendous response. I also contacted Judith Thwaite and Don Ayers through a cancer support group leaflet that I picked up in the library. They jointly edit a publication called Patchwork, which compiles various poetry and written works for and by cancer sufferers. They sent me batches of the publication to review; I picked various pieces that I was interested in and they helped me to contact the contributing authors. I received other entries from adverts in the press from all over the UK. I also contacted a variety of people whose work I had seen in other publications who agreed to write pieces for the book.

It all sounds very straightforward but I can assure it wasn't plain sailing. As I have never published a book before in my life, I can honestly tell you that it was, as my Dad would say, 'a character building experience'. My Dad says this phrase when anybody moans about a situation, so as to draw a positive from a negative experience and this became the inspiration for the title as it fits with the ethos of the book.

I have really enjoyed compiling this book and talking to the authors and learning about their lives. I hope that when you read this book that its purpose is successful in inspiring you to lead life to the full and understand that we need bad times to know what are the good times. In addition, I would also like you to see that adversity can only ever build upon your character and make you a stronger person when you emerge from the other side. If you are going through a difficult time I hope you see that you are not alone and I hope that this book will help you believe that there is light at the end of the tunnel.

Anna Walker
(TV Presenter)
⌘
Character Building

By the time I ended my teenage years, my character was well and truly built.

My mother died of breast cancer on Christmas day, three weeks after I turned eighteen. Watching her deal stoically with the pain, the treatment and the indignity of losing her looks, her hair and her breast, made me feel small, but inspired.

What would I have done in her shoes? Would I have simply crawled into a hole, given up hope and cried myself to sleep? Or could I have found the strength, as she did, to carry on every day, knowing those days were numbered?

Never complaining, never demanding; but simply wanting to spend precious moments with those she loved, with as much laughter as she could handle. Not for her the 'sensible' option of staying at home in bed, until she took her last breath. No, she preferred to take the whole family to South Africa for what she knew would be her last Christmas.

That was the country where she had began married life with my father. His cousin, Daphne, and her best friend, Hilda, still lived there. Despite doctor's warnings that the trip would kill her, she decided to spend the last days of her life surrounded by the people who mattered most, in a country she loved.

It was all a bit unreal; pushing her on the plane in her wheelchair, meeting these people who had meant so much to her and feeling embarrassed by their shocked tears. Lying in the hot sun in wintertime, I wished the trip could last forever. I now realise she was shielding us from reality...rather than tarnishing everything that was familiar to us and waiting for the inevitable. She wanted to create more fond memories, and allow us to return to our lives as if awakening from a dream.

We celebrated Christmas on Christmas Eve that year, with Hilda's family in Cape Town. Never had turkey tasted so good, or the laughter been so loud. We went to bed smiling and were woken early with news that Mum had died that night. The immense sadness I felt at her loss was tempered by the fact that she had chosen to go that way.

Now, whenever I am tempted to moan about my lot, I'll think of what Mum suffered without complaint and realise that I'm blessed. I'm convinced I would be a different (and lesser) person if I hadn't witnessed the dignity and strength with which my Mum faced cancer.

I'm just one of many you'll read about in this book, who are fortunate to have known incredible people who have inspired others to push themselves beyond what they thought they were capable of.

Far from being depressing, this book should make you want to get out there and do something you've always wanted to do but always put off until another day. If there's a message it's this...love life, and live each day as if it was your last.

Most importantly, if you're reading this it means you've contributed to the 'Cancer Research Campaign', which is dedicated ultimately to finding a cure for cancer. Until that goal is achieved, we must console ourselves that there are some remarkable people who have shown tremendous courage in the face of adversity.

Rudyard Kipling

⌘

IF

If you can keep your head when all about you
Are losing theirs and blaming it on you,
If you can trust yourself when all men doubt you,
But make allowance for their doubting too;

If you can wait and not be tired by waiting,
Or being lied about, don't deal in lies,
Or being hated, don't give way to hating,
And yet don't look too good, nor talk too wise:

If you can dream—and not make dreams your master;
If you can think — and not make thoughts your aim;
If you can meet with Triumph and Disaster
And treat those two impostors just the same;

If you can bear to hear the truth you've spoken
Twisted by knaves to make a trap for fools,
Or watch the things you gave your life to, broken,
And stoop and build 'em up with worn-out tools:

If you can make one heap of all your winnings
And risk it on one turn of pitch-and-toss,
And lose, and start again at your beginnings
And never breathe a word about your loss;

If you can force your heart and nerve and sinew
To serve your turn long after they are gone,
And so hold on when there is nothing in you
Except the will, which says to them: 'Hold on!'

14

If you can talk with crowds and keep your virtue,
Or walk with Kings—nor lose the common touch,
If neither foes nor loving friends can hurt you,
If all men count with you, but none too much;

If you can fill the unforgiving minute
With sixty seconds' worth of distance run,
Yours is the Earth and everything that's in it,
And—which is more—you'll be a Man, my son!

Margaret Seed has had breast and bowel cancer since 1993 as well as secondaries. She has found the best way to reach out and help other people in similar situations is to share her thoughts in writing. Margaret has had great support from family and friends and feels extremely lucky for that. However, she feels that the best way to fight is from within. She says it has been the most difficult thing she has ever had to deal with but·has come to realise that you have to keep fighting. Her experience has made her look at life differently and she now appreciates more of what she previously took for granted like going for walks and enjoying the scenery. The two main things she has learnt are that people matter and that you have to be positive in your outlook to be able to fight.

Margaret Seed

⌘

Understanding Cancer

This is going to be a very honest story but I have to admit I am not, never have been and never will be a writer. What I am is someone who, since 1993, has had breast and bowel cancer and secondaries and has survived. So what? you may ask, there are plenty of people going through the same, why write about it? My answer is that I believe everyone should have the chance to know true support and the understanding that comes from knowing you are not alone in feeling the way you do and that there is still life after being diagnosed with cancer. Having gone through and lived with the turmoil cancer inflicts, not only on us patients, but the whole family, I really feel I would like to be there for everyone going through this turmoil at present. As this is physically impossible I decided the best and only way to reach you all would be by sharing my thoughts with you in writing.

Not everyone is fortunate enough to have the magnificent support from family and friends that I have had. Yes, I have been extremely lucky and will be forever grateful, but the fact remains there are a lot of frightened, lonely people having to cope with a life-threatening illness that shows no discrimination in age, sex or affluence. It does not matter if you are rich or poor, old or young, good or bad. When cancer strikes, whatever our social circumstances, we all have one common aim — to get treated as quickly as possible and remain healthy for as long as possible.

Coming to terms with any life-threatening disease is far from easy. Being told you have got cancer is hard to take in. Emotions run deep. Questions are asked, not only of yourself, but also by yourself as to why me? How long have I got? Could they have got it wrong? Etc., etc.

Then when realisation sets in, there are the doubts – What can I do? Who do I see? What are my best options? Finally it hits home that all this is real, you are not dreaming and tomorrow is another day – a day that needs fighting for and, more importantly, living for. Fighting is easy isn't it? There are many things daily in life that have to be fought for, but surely now the battle is greater and somewhere you have to find the strength to get into the ring and fight to the end. Without doubt the best way to fight is from within. Everyone else can support from outside, but I genuinely believe that the greatest support of all comes from yourself. That does not mean that other people cannot help. Indeed family and friends are an essential part and play an important role in the winning game. No one knows this more than I do. I have had magnificent support from my family and friends and if I was in the boxing ring myself and had just won a fight, as with all boxers, I would be thanking all my family and friends for their encouragement and support. But what happens if someone has to go through all this alone?

We all know someone or have heard of someone who has cancer.

The word conjures up fear in the minds of the most healthy, so you can imagine what it does to the person who has just been told they have become a victim of one of the most unwanted diseases of the twentieth century. It doesn't matter how long it takes to be told of this diagnosis or how nicely this is done, you are still left with a feeling that this is not happening to you. It is as if the mind takes longer than any part of the body for such news to register. Some people, on being told of the diagnosis, break down straight away and deal with this the best way they can until they arrive home. Others, still in shock, say 'thank you very much' out of sheer politeness, go home and collapse into a friendly environment in the hope that this was all a dream and can't possibly be happening.

The next important step forward and the most frustrating of all is what I call the waiting game. Waiting for appointments, waiting for opinions, waiting for results and confirmation that you have been worrying legitimately or not. Waiting for the all-important referral on to wherever is necessary and, if appropriate, waiting for a hospital bed.

Eventually the waiting is over and the day arrives when the final results and explanations are given to us and we are advised to try not to worry. Why is it that all the thousands of questions we had in our minds now come out as a jumbled mess and, by the time composure sets in, everyone has gone and another day has to be got through?

I honestly do not want any of this to sound depressing, so you may wonder why I have decided to put it all down in black and white.

I believe nobody can fully understand what it is like to have cancer unless you have been there and worn the T-shirt. Sometimes, even when you are or have been there, you still wonder if everyone else in your position has the same fears, questions, etc. You wonder how other people handle being told they have cancer, then live with it - Can you get through this? Is there going to be any quality of life left? etc., etc. Sometimes it seems as if nobody understands how you feel, but really how can anyone who has not been in the same position be expected to understand? I have been there and remember the feelings of anger, despair, helplessness and fear, so I thought it might help anyone going through similar circumstances to see you can get through it with positive thinking and determination.

Yes, I would be lying if I said dealing with cancer is a piece of cake. Far from it, it is the most difficult thing I have ever had to deal with. Over the past five years there have been many ups and downs, but the main message I have got out of all of this is that there are no prizes for giving in. I admit sometimes it would be a lot easier to give in, but then anything as important as life and living has to be worth fighting for, hasn't it? Really, everyone should live on a daily basis; no one knows what is round the corner. Instead, we all think and expect there is plenty of time left to do whatever we want to and hopefully this is the case for many, many people.

However, it doesn't mean when you are told you have got cancer that life has to stop. In many ways we look at life differently. We appreciate more of what previously we took for granted. People talk about winning the lottery or having lots of money. Okay, it would be nice to have no money worries but money can't buy health, peace of mind or, indeed, any of the important things in life. When you get up tomorrow, be positive about whatever you decide to do. Enjoy and appreciate the little things in life, listening to the birds, going for a walk.

Enjoy the free air and scenery that, before we were diagnosed, we all took for granted.

If there is one thing that I have learned over the past five years it is that people matter. Your priorities change overnight and you realise how many important things you have and don't want to lose. Why should we lose them? Why should we give in and let this horrible disease win? We must all fight and be positive, the mind is a wonderful piece of equipment that we all possess and I firmly believe that a healthy mind helps to promote a healthy body.

Unfortunately, I do not know you personally, so I cannot know how cancer has affected your life. If you are a relative of someone with cancer I can only hope that what has been said has given you some insight as to what being told you have cancer feels like. As patients, we fully realise and appreciate it is far from easy for partners, family and friends to know how to help someone close who is suffering from cancer, but please never think we don't need your support, love and friendship. We always have and always will need and be grateful for the tender, loving care and understanding given.

If you are a patient in hospital or an outpatient at the moment, I hope this story helps give you the encouragement and will to be positive. You can get through this and I know you will. You may feel like you are being put through the wringer but you can come out the other side. I did and so can you. So go for it.

If you are living with cancer I hope reading this will help you. You can still enjoy life, you can get through anything with a positive mind, and every hurdle can be jumped. Please go for it, as I am doing, give it your best shot and together let's show this unwanted disease it has a real fight on its hands and we intend to win that fight.

Norman Ford was born in

Southampton, in 1924 and was the youngest of five children. He gained a scholarship to Taunton's Grammar school in 1934, he first published a poem in the school Magazine Literary Supplement the same year. He went on to gain another scholarship to go to University College in 1941, did war service from 1942-5 and was on active service with the Hampshire and Devon Regiments. He took an English Honours Degree with London university in 1948 and then trained as a secondary teacher. He retired as head of English in 1988. He has been a political activist and Parish councillor and his hobbies are writing, music and entertaining. Norman has been a widower since 1998.

Norman Ford

⌘

Surviving

Dear Queen, I was sad when they told me that you
Had been having annus horribilus too,
So I thought you might find it some comfort to hear
That it's not been exactly my favourite year.

First they chopped out my tumour,
("the size of an egg!")
I had jabs in my buttocks, my arm and my leg;
I had probes down my throat and
Then tubes up my nose,
And I learned where the end of a catheter goes.

I had masking with plaster and deep radiation,
Severe diarrhoea and acute constipation;
I took thousands of tablets, and became very knowledgy
'bout the meanings of rude-sounding words like "oncology".

They did things I can't mention without sounding crude,
And solved my weight problems...I just stopped eating food!
Now roast beef and Yorkshire can ne'er pass my lips,
And I've forgotten the flavour of sausage and chips.

When I was working, I often would say:
"I wouldn't have her job for double the pay!"

Now, glandless, I never will know how it feels
to attend all those banquets and eat all those meals.

Like you I've got problems, but no use to grouse!
At least no one, so far, has burned down my house;
No cameras appear when I try to relax,
And, as far as I know I don't owe any tax.

So chin up, Your Queenship, and be of good cheer,
We're not what we were, but at least we're still
here.
But one thought, I'm certain I share, Ma'am, with
you: I don't want another ...1992!

Norman Ford

⌘

Late Love

I once trudged through the wood in the winter,
Beneath boughs that were blackened and bare;
And the trees like some war-weary giants
Seemed to throw up their arms in despair.

And the soldiers that scoured that woodland
Were as scarred as the branches above;
For their hearts carried death like the weapons they
bore;
And they thought more of vengeance than love.

When I walked in a wood in the springtime,
Wild primroses bloomed at my feet,
And the trees, full of promise, stretched welcoming
arms,
Inviting young sweethearts to meet.

When I walked in a wood in the summer,
I heard laughter and fond lovers' sighs,
As they basked in the leaf-filtered sunshine,
Believing young love never dies.

Now I stroll through those woods in that season
Whose beauty outshines all the rest,
When life, like the leaves, so precariously poised,
Seems at it's eye-dazzling best.

And the love that we find in the autumn,
Is the rarest and the fairest of all.
Surely nothing can equal the magic
Of leaves, life and love in the fall.

Norman Ford

⌘

No Caviar For Me,
Thanks - I'm Thriving!

I was never a gourmet. With a modest expertise in the culinary art; I could prepare a reasonable roast and do justice to it along with the next man. But I had little patience with the enthusiastic food freak who would go into raptures about the delicious chicken fricassee they served down at the "Dog and Duck. Food, for me, was a necessary part of the daily routine, forgotten as soon as devoured.

That was before I was put into the medical mincer, prodded and processed, in preparation for having my tenderest parts roasted in the radio-therapy micro-wave, to emerge as an over-done scrag-end of my former self, quite unable to cope with those complicated tasks of everyday life, like walking, sitting, sleeping, bathing, drinking and dancing the hokey-cokey. Oh, and, I nearly forgot...eating.

I have, I am happy to report, re-acquired all those skills, except dancing the hokey-cokey and...eating. Well, eating in any civilised sense of the word. I can, I'm pleased to say, swallow soup, soup, soup, ice-cream, custard, jelly, soup, liquidised all-bran, soup, and an occasional delightful tin of En-sure (which is a kind of. . . .er, soup!).

I will not bore you with the medical explanation of this condition; only urge you never to disparage your saliva. It is not there only for when Noel Edmonds comes on the television screen. And, above all, girls, whatever "Slimming World" may say, never undervalue the simple pleasure of eating!

Food, I now realise, lies at the heart of all civilised existence. A fried egg is a fit subject for poetry far superior to Wordsworth's daft daffodils and Westminster Bridge. If you must have literary inspiration, turn rather to men with sensible names like Francis Bacon or Charles Lamb: Here's a theme for a new classic sonnet: "Hail to thee, thou well-cooked meat-and-two-veg! Thou art more to be prized than the wealth of Solomon. A fresh cheese sandwich hath more lustre than the Koh-i-noor." But there are more practical reasons to praise food.

Far from being a self-indulging luxury, eating brings a puritan order and discipline to our chaotic lives, distinguishing hot-roast Sunday from cold-beef Monday and hopeful, fish-fingered dawn from romantic, French cuisined eve. What greater admission of brutishness could there be than serving corn flakes at the Vicar's tea party?

Talk of food can be as beguiling as the murmurings of love. What Tchaikovsky melody could match the sweetness of: "Tea ready. Toast and marmalade on the table!" Could Plato or Socrates pose a weightier philosophical question than: "What shall we have for dinner tomorrow?"? Think of the heavy tasks made bearable by a brisk: "Kettle's on. Do you like rock-cakes?" or "Have a break - have a Kit-kat!"

Then there are those life-long relationships sparked off by an invitation to "Come over for lunch on Sunday" and new adventures opened by an eager: "Let's walk by the river. We can have a ploughman's at the pub." What exciting careers are launched (or unhappy ones terminated) by the call to meet the new boss over a buffet lunch!

Don't misunderstand me. I'm not ungrateful to those wonderful doctors and nurses who removed food from my agenda in order to snatch me from the arms of the Grim Reaper - allowing him to claim only my saliva glands. But just as the deaf Beethoven hoped he would "hear in Heaven", it would be very nice if, when the Great Call comes, I am able to respond positively to that celestial choir singing: "Fancy a good chicken fricassee? They do a divine one up here at the 'Dog and Duck'!"

Tom Bidwell was born in Stockport, in 1984 and now lives in Leyland. He was diagnosed with T-cell Non Hodgkins Lymphoma in January 1999 and has spent many weeks being treated at both Manchester Children's Hospital and The Christie. Now two years after his treatment he is still writing, but claims that he has 'come a long way' as a writer since 1999. He is currently co-writing a musical and writing songs on the guitar, while studying for his final year of A-levels at Runshaw College, Leyland. His ambition, to be able to fly, is still unrealised.

Tom Bidwell

⌘

There's People Worse Off

There's people worse off than you in the world
When you're sat at home with "the flu"
People in Africa starving and dying
While you're sat with your tissues moaning and crying
You get clean water without even trying
There's people worse off than you

Yes there's people worse off than you in the world
When your love romance falls through
There's people in wars, ripped apart at the seams
People in wheelchairs losing their dreams
And look at you now trying to make a scene
There's people worse off than you

There's people worse off than you in the world
When you need some clothes that are new
People all over cursed with disease
Children in India, down on their knees
And you're annoyed 'cos your clothes don't please!
There's people worse off than you

Tom Bidwell

⌘

The Bitter Truth

Sometimes I wonder about our race,
Which has a materialistic face.
Do they ever stop and contemplate,
About such things as life and fate?

Or do they just accept it so,
And hold the line, which they must tow?
Why do we all let this fraud be?
Discard your money and TV!

Our lives are wasted in an attempt to impress,
The way we act, the way we dress.
The things we say, the things we know.
Does it really matter though?

Who cares who's right? Who cares who's wrong?
Let's learn the words to a different song.
If we threw away the superficial cover,
We'd see the world; we'd see each other.

Tom Bidwell
⌘
The Path

Imagine you are in a beautiful wood. When you take your first step you hear the crunching of pine needles under your feet and sunbeams flow through the breaks in the trees above. The floor is a brown carpet of pine needles, which were placed so perfectly last fall. Bursting out of the rusty brown coloured floor there are patches of bright green grass with blue bells growing in them.

As you continue you notice a break in the trees ahead and, as the tall pines thin out, you stop on a soft patch of grass. As you glance up the sun is blazing in all its glory in a perfect ocean blue sky. The grass you are standing on is at the top of a short cliff, which looks across thousands of daffodils and tulips, which sway gently in the breeze. At the immediate base of the cliff is a pool filled with cool, clear water. Butterflies of all colours fly haphazardly over it and rest on the blooming flowers around it. The flowers appear to be tropical and have enormous, unusually sized petals on them. They create a myriad of colours and their perfume fills your senses. In the pool, fish glide around making the occasional splash and upsetting the stillness of the water. The only sound you hear are the birds singing high in the sky and the slight breeze rustling through the pines, which is quite refreshing in the sun.

There is a small mud track leading down the cliff, which obviously hasn't been used for some time, as the grass is beginning to re-grow. You follow the path down to a field, which is full of ferns and several different types of tall grasses. The grass is about shoulder high so it is difficult to walk through. But you continue to do so, not knowing where the path (which you can barely make out) may lead you.

The track leads on through the field until the grass stops suddenly and you see the ground and now tread is hard, dry mud. Suddenly you feel cold and realise you are out of the sun. As you look up you become aware that you are standing in the shadow of a gigantic tree. Its huge branches are foreboding and appear as sinewy arms, thick and twisting like rope, holding handfuls of burgundy coloured leaves. Its bark is deep brown and its trunk is ten feet in diameter. It reminds you of a tree out of a fairy tale filled with magic and enchantment. However, as it stares at you, there is something unnatural about it. It seems to be a freak, out of place in the beauty of the fields, but there it stands looming over you, sending a certain coldness through you. But you continue to stare, standing almost hypnotised as you get lost in the strangeness of this towering outcast.

The path leads on through more fields, fields of blazing red tulips and golden daffodils, but you don't follow it. Stepping back from the tree, although beastly, there seems something almost majestic about it and you seem content to stare, stood in its wake.

The moral to this story is simple. The path is the metaphor of life. The fields represent good times and the tree bad times. In this story you dwelled on the tree and skipped by all the beauty of the pool and the wood. Don't dwell on bad memories the past cannot be changed, but the future is yours to mould. Walk past the tree and through the fields and who knows what you may find.

Carol McGruer grew up in Aberdeen but now resides with her husband Gordon in Cheshire, nearby her family. She has a son and daughter and one grandchild. Her interests are country music, travelling and needlework and is an active member of a local quilting group. She has also recently completed a computer course at Macclesfield College. The poem was written when she was at school when given a title and tasked with writing an appropriate poem.

Carol McGruer

⌘

Broken Heart

A welcome voice upon the phone
Forget for a while I'm on my own
Our troubles we have often shared
Our souls to each other we have bared

I think my hurt has been so great
To start again it is too late
My heart I will not risk again
From Cupid's match I will refrain

She says how that is such a waste
Because one woman's been too faced
Don't give up on life's merry dance
Surely loves worth another chance

Just now is too soon to think that way
Wrapped in my hardened shell I stay
Alone just now my heart still raw
Perhaps one day this ice will thaw

Through the traffic homeward bound
In my head those thoughts go round
Another evening on my own
Perhaps a voice upon the phone

The rooms feel so very cold
Is this my lot when I am old?
To sit alone with saddened heart
Because my family is apart

The weekend comes again at last
The children bring alive the past
Good times, bad times before me flash
These hours together soon will pass

I leave them now and turn away
Oh Daddy, please why can't you stay?
My heart is heavy as I turn the key
What hell life is with no family.

Dorothy Rowlands was born in Manchester in 1942 and currently cares for her husband who suffers from a muscular disease. She attended university at the age of fifty and obtained a management degree before her husband required more attention. In addition, she is on the Princess Royal Trust carers committee and also helps at her local school as an assistant, teaching seven-year-olds English and Maths. Dorothy will be retiring in March 2002 and has joined a writing group to learn more about her hobby. She has two daughters and two grandchildren with whom she spends a lot of time. Earlier this year she entered the Cancer Research Campaign competition 'Write for Life' and took third place out of ten thousand entries with her poem about carers and won five hundred pounds.

Dorothy Rowlands
⌘
The Last Valentine

I dream this day of youth; of holding hands on
evening walks and contemplating lifelong plans.
Holding tight our wedding rings; I think of passion
long since spent, to be replaced by love that lingers
on through life.

I give my thanks for all your tender care; for years
of toil, for being there when needed most.
I dream with fondness and with sorrow of our life.
And, as I recall our memories I thank the Lord for
sparing you, you gave me strength to share it all, for
I can truly say, "I love you."

I think of years long lost, of fighting, killing, war.
I dream of how returning home, defeated, weary
battle sore, you helped me heal.
I think of babies now full grown.
Beloved babes with children of their own.

I dream of feelings shared throughout the years;
The angers, sorrows, all the pain and fears of
growing old.
And now, some senses gone, when sight will fade
and hearing dim;
Our love lives on.

We can bequeath no large amounts of monies, gains
or land.
But yet my love I'm proud to die a very wealthy man,

For having loved you.
And now dear heart my life is done, and I have no
regrets, I'll stand aside and proudly wait; beyond
the heavens eternal gates,
For I have truly loved you.

Matthew Blake

⌘

Overcoming Cancer

At the age of 17 every teenager should have the world at their feet, but unlike any normal teenager I had to have a setback.

I was an ordinary 17-year-old who loved to play sports, swim competitively and enjoyed life to the full. It was about 1993 I noticed I was getting more out of breath playing football, but thought nothing of it. I just trained harder as I thought that my fitness was failing. Later on, when my mum noticed a lump on my neck, I thought that it was muscle as it did not hurt and felt like muscle. After a while I went to the doctors to satisfy my mother's worry, thinking nothing of it. At the time I was studying for my A-levels (Sociology, Geography and Economics).

The blood results came back and they thought it was glandular fever but wanted to do a biopsy on it. This is when I started to get worried. I had the biopsy and the news was broken to my parents (not me) which blew the wind out of their sails, not to mention that they diagnosed it as cancer but a different strain which indicated that I may not have long left to live. Even the consultant who looked at the chest x-ray results could not believe that I was the same person in front of him. I also had bone marrow taken, the most painful experience of my life, luckily that was clear.

Eventually after the biggest shock of my life and lots of saying 'why me?' and 'what do I say to everyone?' and 'how long have I got left?' I got the correct diagnosis of Hodgkin's disease. After a few nights out on the beer I started to accept that I would have to have this thing called chemotherapy which makes your hair fall out and makes you sick. (Well, that is how the media portrayed it.) I found that it was my parents who were worst affected. They felt responsible, as if they could have done something different in my life to have changed the events. They also felt helpless as they could do nothing for me since it was now all down to the hospital staff. My closest friends were great, they carried on as normal but some people don't know how to react and keep their distance in case it is catching but life goes on. Back then the 'C' word was deadly and heaven forbid you got it, as you were as good as dead.

I had six months of chemo. I did not want to lose my hair, but tough, it went and you just got on with it. I continued my A-levels and had the odd morning off for my chemo. Yeah, I felt ill at times and knackered but I just counted down the amounts of treatments I had left and looked forward to no more treatment. I left sixth form at 19 with 2 out of 3 A-levels, one being a B, not bad for someone who had a bit more on his plate than the other guys.

I wanted to go to university like my brother, but because of all my check-ups, I thought that I would put it off for a year. I worked in a sports centre for a year, but no sooner had I had the all clear and started this job, it came back. This time I had radiotherapy, not as intense as chemo but it made my armpits sore and took away most of my hair again as my chest area was being treated. The only time off work I had was to go to the hospital, but radiotherapy I could cope with.

The all clear came (again) and I got my place at Luton University to read Sport and Fitness Science. At last I could start my life again. I met my long-term girlfriend at university and life could not have been any better. I graduated in 1997 with a 2:1 with honours. I stayed living in Luton for a while as I made lots of friends down there, one being a police officer. After speaking with him for hours about the job I thought this sounds like the job for me, so I started to apply.

In the winter of 1997 I started to feel ill. I had night sweats with the window open in January! So I decided to up roots from Luton and return home to Norwich. I went skiing that January in 1998 and felt ill all week but soldiered on; it felt like I had a bad dose of the flu. I then started to have stomach pains and could not sit, stand still or lie down without being in agony, I was also jaundiced. I lost 2 stone in 2 weeks and, yes, it had come back after all this time. I was gutted. I was told I was to have more chemo then see how it goes. I told my consultant to stuff it; I could not handle another 6 to 8 months of chemo and losing my hair again. The only thing that swayed me was that he told me that I would see the coming summer but no more if I refused treatment. After I cooled down I agreed to the unknown again. I had just started a new job driving all over the country erecting promotional stands, the company were great as they let me go part time in between treatments. After six months the cancer still had not fully gone from my abdomen area. I was referred to Addenbrookes Hospital then for a newish treatment called 'stem cell' replacement. This is where your white cells are removed and cleaned and then strong chemo is given to you which kills your immune system and then your white cells are re-infused and start growing in the bone marrow again. I had a small Hickman line put in my neck area, which was used to collect my white blood cells. Then I was admitted to hospital in a sterile room. I was ill from the day I had my first of 3 days of chemo. Then it was waiting until my white cell count died, at which time the white cells could be re-infused. As the immune system dies you pick up infections and go off food.

My friends were great again, coming to see me several times a week, and telling me their problems, which only minor to them, took my mind off my situation. My girlfriend and parents came to see me every day which I looked forward to, but I never told them that as I felt so sorry for myself, even going to the toilet was a day out event which was too much like hard work. Whilst in hospital I got a blood clot in the shoulder which extended my stay even longer. The staff were great though, so I could not complain as I was in the hands of the experts. I was told that it would take about two years to get my immune system back to nearly normal, even though I would always be more susceptible to catching illnesses. When I left I was a shadow of my former self, but at least I got out alive. Shortly afterwards I split with my girlfriend. The stresses and strains were too much, I think, but we are still very close as she helped me through so much.

After the space of a few weeks I was exercising, only walking, but it was a start. I applied for the police after about 6 months but was flatly turned down. I could not understand at the time. After a year my checks were going ok, I was training again, but still the police said that they needed 2 years clear for the medical before they would entertain me, but I continued to pursue them. In the mean time I got a job in a call centre, 6 months after coming out of hospital, my first full time job. After my two years of being all clear passed, I was onto the police again. I got interviews and finally on the 6th November 2000 I was accepted for the Police Force and started training. I had achieved this goal despite the setbacks. I also wanted to purchase a property but because of my medical history thought that this was an impossibility; but earlier this year I bought my very first house. It has taken nearly 10 years, but I have battled on as I have had goals to aim for. Even though I thought of giving up at times, I carried on because of the support of my friends and family.

I hope that if someone reads this it will give them encouragement that there is hope and loads of it. Nowadays there are so many more treatments than there were back then when I was first diagnosed. Nearly everyone knows of someone who has been affected by cancer. It is not a taboo subject now, thanks to people talking about it.

Don Ayers lives with Deborah, in a little cottage, in idyllic surroundings, high in the Derbyshire hills of the High Peak. Ten years ago, whilst he was in Christie's Hospital, he met with fellow poet and patient, Judith Thwaite. Together they began work on an idea that has rolled on into a phenomenon – poetry as a therapy, comfort and inspiration for cancer patients, mourners and the many that survive this illness.

Don is in all three categories – he was a sufferer and also a mourner, for his sister, Sylvia. She had helped him through the darkest days of his illness, only to die of breast cancer herself, a little while later. He is also a survivor, and he believes, very strongly, that writing has played a major role in survival.

Don has worked for many years as a senior lecturer in Creative Arts. Most of his work was concerned with training people to work creatively with people who have disabilities. Although already aware of the therapeutic value of the creative arts, little did he realise how much they would become a therapy in his own life.

When he heard that he had cancer, his first thoughts, like many other cancer sufferers, were: How long have I got? Is it weeks, months or perhaps a year? Will I be able to see the daffodils again, at Ullswater, in the coming springtime?

Well, after ten daffodil springtimes, and after editing and illustrating forty quarterly editions of 'Patchwork', Don is still very much alive. He is busy writing, painting and acting; and somehow manages to find time to visit disabled people with his therapy dog 'Sophie', and to help them with their writing, too.

He says, that one of the positive things about cancer, is that it can motivate you into living life to the full, every minute of every day. Cancer doesn't only take life, it can give life back.

Don Ayers
⌘
Cancer

Then

'Cancer'
a word unuttered,
Cancer:
No, no, my mind is shuttered.

Cancer:
Friends disconcerted,
Their eyes averted,
Scurrying away,
Not knowing how to say,
'Cancer'

Chilling,
Conversation killing,
Cancer

Cancer:
A dreadful, fear instilling
The minds of men and women.

Cancer.

62

And Now

Cancer
Has redeemed me
From complacency
And mundane apathy.
Cancer
Has been my liberation
From convention
And contention.

Cancer
Has broadened my
Understanding and humility,
Deepened my compassion
And humanity.

Cancer
Has made me introspective,
More reflective
And widened
My whole perspective.

Cancer
Has given me strength of purpose;
Made my life more adventurous;
Given me worthy aims to pursue;
Opened new horizons;
Brought new friends, too.

Cancer
Has allowed time to meditate,
To concentrate on things worthwhile
And to create.

Cancer
Has strengthened and enriched
The love and trust
Within a partnership.

Cancer
Has given me direction and a goal.

Cancer
Has awakened
My sleeping soul.

Don Ayers

⌘

Nil By Mouth
reads the sign above my bed.

Never, in all my smoking years, could
I ever of imagined that one day I would be
Lying, here, in this infirmary,
    waiting, and for the tenth time,
Bathed and bedecked to shock, in a backless
Yellow hospital smock,
    waiting, and for the tenth time,
Making out that, as operations go, "I am quite an
Old soldier, don't you know?"
Unfortunately, no one is really listening to me,
They are busy eating lunch and drinking tea, as I,
Hungry, oh so very hungry, lie
    waiting and for the tenth time.

Oh if only, in my smoking years
Each cigarette pack had
Had this warning on the back-
'NIL BY MOUTH'

Don Ayers
⌘
Ward A5

Monday:
I watched you
As you walked away,
Carrying my case;
Home to face
A lonely week,
And I will miss you, too.

From my hospital bed, I view
The white, drawn faces
Of cathetered men
And wonder when
I will leave this place,
To be back home with you.

Through the long night,
I lie awake,
Knowing, tomorrow, they operate.
Tired and sleepless, I wait;
Frantically, I pray
That everything will be alright.

Tuesday:
On a trolley, I wait
In medicated calmness
And perpetually impaired;
All around is rather blurred.
I lie wondering
What will be my fate.

Conscious of voices,
I am lying almost awake,
Back comfortably in bed,
With only one thought in my head:
I am through the operation,
My heart rejoices.

Thursday:
In his dementia, an old man fights
The night staff, whom he curses,
Shouting and swearing.
The strain is wearing
On the patients and nurses.
Another sleepless night.

Friday:
Today it is time to leave.
I talk with fellow patients, now my friends,
Then wait impatiently
Until you come for me.
I say goodbyes, my stay here ends,
I sigh with great relief.

Going home is such a thrill.
Aching and worn,
I hold you tearfully,
And in soaring ecstacy,
I feel reborn:
Stepping out
Of 'Stepping Hill'.

Don Ayers
⌘
Sarsaparilla

'For Health and Long Life,
It Purifies the blood.'
'I'll try some', the Patient said,
'It sounds really, very good'

The G.P. thought his prompt referral
Must have saved the day.

'It was my early diagnosis.'
The Consultant was heard to say.

'It was I,' Said the Surgeon,
As he put away his knife,
'Who cut out the deadly tumour
That was threatening his life.'

'It was the radiotherapy
That burnt each cancerous cell,
And that,' said the Radiotherapist,
'Is why he's done so well.'

'But we supported him,
Through all those awful years,'
Said Family and Friends,
'We held him in our prayers.'

'We Nurses too, throughout those years,
Gave him out constant care.'
'It was my love,' his Lover said,
'And simply being there.'

The Patient thought it was his love
Of life, and for his lover too;
But he read the bottle label,
And then he really knew.

'Not one, but all are listed here,' he said,
'Each has played a part.
For this healing Sarsaparilla,
I thank you with all my heart!'

Don Ayers
⌘
Stonyford

Winter, and a bitterly cold morning.
A flock of sheep, baa-ing and bleating,
Are hustled up the lane,
Their nostrils and fleeces steaming
In the chilling air.

A veil of freezing fog drapes the hills
And fills the quiet valley,
Shortening the visible world,
Curtaining the view;
The days are shorter, too.

And, in this cold capsule of stillness,
I remember the winter of my illness:
The world, was then, a hospital ward
And days shortened by fatigue and fear.
Was it three years ago? It feels so near.

In the garden, a blackbird flits down
And chisels at the icy ground;
A robin bobbing all around,
Finding what food is to be found;
Two blue tits are searching for a scrap.

I go indoors, hang up my coat and cap.
Three cats nestle, purring on my lap;
A log fire crackles and blazes;
There is a good soup in the pan.
I can enjoy this winter, I know I can.

Don Ayers

⌘

Extracts From My Journal

9ᵗʰ April 1999

A lovely, warm, sunny day. It feels more like summer than spring. The first, free, fine day for quite sometime so I decide to attack our overgrown, cottage garden. The rains of the past weeks have created a dense, green jungle. But where to start? Huge leaves of a variegated ivy are blocking light to the small window of the lounge and long tendrils are stretching right up to the stone slates of the roof. Here we go! – I tug at the thick arm of the ivy near the window and it breaks away from the wall. A startled, hen blackbird bursts from the ivy just above my head. The clump of ivy I have torn from the wall has revealed her nest. I stand on tiptoe and peer into the nest. I can see four, speckled, greenish-blue eggs in the nest. The nest is a carefully woven basket; small twigs on the outer side and straw grass inside, bound together with brown earth. There are a few small feathers and even a few strands of gold, florist's ribbon – here is a blackbird with a penchant for interior design!

I wonder how, living so close to the window, they have coped with the nightly, booming beat, as Deborah plays her John Lee Hooker's discs at full volume. Maybe they are Blues lovers, too!

1st May 1999

A lovely, fresh, sunny morning. The fledgling blackbirds left their nest a few days ago and have been hiding amongst the holly and hawthorn whilst the parent birds have flown endlessly, to and fro, with tasty morsels for them.

At least one fledgling has fallen prey to the feral cats that visit our garden at night-time. I have tried very hard to keep Hamish, our silver tabby cat, and Sophie, our keen-nosed Samoyed, out of the way, but this morning each joins the hunt and each adds to the blackbird's death toll. I feel very angry with what they have done. I tell Deborah, she is angry too. We both have strong words with Sophie and Hamish, they are in disgrace.

Deborah, thinks that the blackbirds will have no further use for the nest and takes the opportunity to clear most of the overgrown ivy from the cottage wall.

It is early evening, the male blackbird is singing from his perch on the power cable above the garden, but not with his usual bright, fruity tone. There is a sadness in his calling, as if he is telling the world, not only of the loss of his young ones, but of the loss of his home, too. But, gradually, the bright, fruity tones find their way back into his song. I listen as he sings and whistle back to him.

2nd May 1999

I awake early this morning. I draw back the curtains and look out from the bedroom window across the garden. The two blackbirds are busy again. She collecting twigs and straw and he, down by the stream, digging mud. They are building a new home in the clematis and honeysuckle on the barn wall.

There is a very obvious moral here. The blackbirds teach us a lot about life.

...If you are feeling low and as though your whole world lies in ruins, let your grief out, then pick up the pieces. 'Life has to go on!' Be like the blackbird and sing (or maybe write a poem) to cheer yourself up. Go on, you can make a fresh start − 'Today is the first day of the rest of your life!'

Sheila Khan aged 49 has written about her fond memories of her friendship from the age of 15 with her best friend Helen, who had breast cancer and following a mastectomy was found with secondaries in her lungs and liver. Sadly before this book went to print Helen passed away. Helen would have been extremely happy to know that Sheila's poem has been published, as she loved the poem. Helen was a happy go lucky person and throughout her illness always maintained her high spirits and sense of humour.

Sheila Khan

⌘

For My Bestest Friend Helen

As I pass along memory lane, back to our teens,
a long time ago? Or yesterday it seems,
we were really starting out on life; yes we had it all,
our youth, our health, our sense of humour, yes we
had a ball.

All our plans we had in mind live life to the full,
Never ever were we down, our lives were never dull.
We'd look out for each other, when on our travels
we did ride,
Not knowing what was in store for us, when for our
lives we had to hide.

We almost met our end, but were lucky to come
through,
All because you had me, and corky I had you.
We'd confide in each other, everyone else was
pushed out.
If we needed one another, we'd simply give a shout.

We eventually went our separate ways, with our
memories put on hold.
Each one of us wondering if we'd meet when we
were old.
We found each other once again reflected on our
past,
We've laughed, and cried, and wished and wished,
our lives hadn't gone so fast.

Oh Nell I want to say what you already know,
I love you like a sister and I don't want you to go,
I'll miss you Nell you know I will, you are a true friend
And I will be by your side right up until the end.

Although we will be apart, we'll be together side by side,
You were always a treasure in you I could confide,
Soul mates that's us a friendship so true,
And if I live my life again, I hope I find you.

Anonymous
⌘
My Dad

My Dad died over three and a half years ago now, when I was seventeen. I miss him more now than I ever have done and I've found writing this very difficult. Dad suffered a heart attack when he was in a 'keep fit' class. By the time Mum and I got to the hospital he was dead. I identified the body. I still don't know if this was a good idea or not but it meant Mum didn't have to do it at least. The last image I have of Dad is of him lying on the hospital trolley with his feet sticking out from under the sheet. I don't remember much about the following weeks except the amount of things that needed organising. I couldn't even tell you which day of the week the funeral was although I could probably work it out if I wanted to.

I don't get upset for me anymore, I get upset for him. He didn't get to see me turn 18 or 21. He didn't get to see any of his kids' graduate from university. He won't see any of us marry or have kids of our own. He never saw the rewards of the things he worked so hard for every day of his life. I worry a lot for my family. Mum is still very angry. I don't understand this but then she was married to him for twenty-seven years. She didn't expect to grow old alone. The day Dad died a huge part of Mum (and my relationship with her) died too. My brother and I are not close. He's never talked to me about his feelings and never would. I just hope he has someone in his life that he can talk to. I worry most for my sister. When Dad died my brother and sister were both at university. Having to tell my sister what happened over the phone is the hardest thing I've ever done in my life, worse than identifying the body or getting through the funeral. Remembering that phone call hurts me so much.

I can't remember the last time I told Dad I loved him. If I had one wish it wouldn't be that he never died, it would be to say thank you to him and to tell him that I love him. Most of all I feel ashamed that I never took the chance to say that when he was here to listen.

I honestly believe that I have been lucky and it helps me a lot to think this way. It all could have been much worse. As far as I know from the people who were with Dad when he died it was all over very quickly. I just hope that this is true. To know that he didn't have time to worry about us (his family) means everything to me. I guess I'm sorry that he had to die but I'm not sorry about the way it happened if that makes sense.

Christine Ridley Henderson

was born in Sunderland in 1947. Christine has been married for thirty years and has two sons. She has written for the book due to her own circumstances and because she loves writing. She has written other poems, which have been published, one about an autistic boy and another about Sunderland new city, which have gone in two other books. She had cancer six years ago and had chemo, since then she's had further treatment for a tumour. She had six treatments in total and lost her hair, which she found difficult, but she has overcome it now. She says thinking positively helped her. She currently takes long-term guests in to live with her and has summer students to stay. Poetry is her main hobby but she is currently enjoying learning about the Internet.

Christine Ridley Henderson
⌘

!!CANCER!!
And so it was

Sudden shock, emotional tears
Diagnosed it was my worst of fears,
"It's Cancer," the registrar quietly said,
I lay devastated! In my hospital bed.
The operation was a different pain,
Cancer, my body didn't feel the same.
Blank, empty, which road from here.
How long, with those that I love dear.
A few days later one afternoon,
my specialist walked into the room,
"I'm extremely confident," said he with a smile,
explaining with detail for a while.
And so my sense of strength came back,
I'll knock this Cancer from it's track.
Chemotherapy, I'm frightened! So what,
I am going to give this all I've got.
I want to live life's highs and low's,
Cancer shall keep me on my toes.
Living with Cancer is what I'll do,
I'm going to see this illness through.
Shattered! When I lost my hair,
a wig does not compare.
But hair it will grow again,
Chemotherapy twice in six years.
I'll not complain,
I feel like a cygnet, but I'll be a swan.
Cancer! What's that! It's gone,
God and specialist work hand in hand,
I'm not yet ready for the Promised Land.

Paula Hadlum was born and lives in Nuneaton. She wrote 'Diagnosis' as part of her writing course. She finds writing a good way of dealing with issues in her life. She came third in 'The Cancer Research' competition. She spends a lot of time writing novels and is a part-time library assistant. She is also studying for a Masters degree in Library management and hopes to become a part time librarian and author.

Paula Hadlum
⌘
The Diagnosis

The doctor was blunt in his diagnosis. "She has asthma," he said and I had to make an incredible leap of faith to believe him. He'd barely examined her. All he'd done was listen to my explanation of her symptoms and laid a stethoscope on her chest. Now suddenly he was declaring asthma.

I'd only come for medicine to ease her cough. I had no intention of going home with an asthmatic three-year-old.

It shouldn't have come as such a great shock. I can recall the wheezing of my mother's asthma long before I even had a name for it. I see myself as nine years old. I picture my sister and myself running up a steep hill. We're chasing after our brand new stepfather. We've almost caught him but he surprises us. He springs round to chase us and we run the other way, screaming in giggles.

Mum's there in the picture. She's halfway up the hill. She looks pale and has to stop. Gripping a knuckled fist to her chest she wheezes a shallow breath and calls for help to walk.

Left to our own devices, we soon grow impatient. We run down the hill and all around them, skipping away and coming back, irritated by the wait. Eventually she finds the breath and lumbers on, leaning heavily on our stepfather and gasping for every step. Her pace is slow. My resentment is rising.

That's asthma to a nine-year-old.

Amy was just three when she brought her unforgiving cough to our new house. I thought it was down to the move. The dust of packing and unpacking. The trace remains of an unfamiliar dog. Until it became so severe she'd lie down wherever she happened to be, and there she'd stay. I'd find her almost straight away, a tiny ball, a mass of knotted blonde in the kitchen or the bathroom. Once I found her on the stairs. Halfway up... like my mother.

That's why, with the house in chaos, I paid a visit to our new doctor, only to be told the news I least wanted. "She has asthma."

I collected the prescription he gave for inhalers and cough medicine but remained cynical of his diagnosis. I couldn't help but wonder if he wasn't jumping a little too high to grab for all the wrong conclusions. To prove it, I followed his every instruction, including an appointment with the asthma nurse. Surely she would be on my side.

Between these visits, Amy had a particularly bad time. She was always worse in the night, but one night her coughing kept us all from sleep. It was past midnight when I hurried across the landing to find her sitting up in bed with a nosebleed. Quick comfort and a damp flannel cleared away the fright.

A dose of cough medicine and a blast of Ventolin persuaded her back to sleep.

For half an hour I lay awake listening. She seemed to settle but the coughing began again and this time there were tears. Her nose was bleeding violently. The sheets and pillowcase were mottled red and her nightdress was saturated. Blood was streaked through her hair, smeared across her face and caked into her hands.

It decided me.

I cleaned and comforted her then piled her in the car. She was calmer now. She enjoyed the short drive to the hospital, chatting and snuggling against the chair while I worked myself up to a quiet frenzy. In casualty she was examined by a doctor. I told him about the asthma, quietly hoping for an alternative diagnosis.

He couldn't persuade this stubborn three-year-old to let him listen to her chest and five minutes later we were on our way home. "Nose bleeds can sometimes be a common symptom of asthma," he said. "She seems better now and there's nothing else we can do."

Of course she was better. She'd been out on a great midnight adventure. The bleeding had stopped, the coughing had eased and all the way home, she was chattering and asking constant questions. She didn't even care about the congealed blood in her hair or the brown stains on her hands.

When I took her to the asthma nurse, and deafened her with my doubts, she listened and smiled the way nurses do. She asked me questions and I gave my answers willingly. I didn't see that all the time she was luring me into a trap. "Would you say she's coughing less now?"

"Definitely."

"And when she does cough, is it as violent?"

"No."

"Which means the Ventolin's working!" She concluded and clang went the jaws of the trap around my naivete. "Does anybody else in the family have asthma?"

"My Nan used to," I replied. "My Mum does. And... er... me!"

I'd been diagnosed asthmatic six years earlier. Caught out by the mother of all April showers, I'd quickly developed a cold that worsened to a chest infection. Two days later, while we were out with the dogs, the breathlessness came on. I tried to ease it by sucking in long breaths but anxiety had constricted my windpipe until I could hardly breathe at all. The fear escalated. The tears began. There was no doubt in my terrified mind: if my breathing didn't ease soon, I would collapse and die.

The doctor I saw was an aged man, abrupt but very experienced. He listened to my explanation and asked if I had asthma. I denied it. "I think you have," he said and gave me a prescription for a Ventolin inhaler and a course of penicillin.

Of course, I went away without believing. Surely there were tests that had to be done. Blood tests, or breath tests or some sort of X-ray. My health had always been good and nobody caught asthma from a rainstorm.

The antibiotics quickly drove out the infection. I soon forgot how frightened I'd been and the inhaler got stowed in a drawer. The next time I caught a cold, and felt it pulling on my chest, I grabbed for another prescription of antibiotics but eyed the Ventolin warily.

I suffered worse during the night. I'd lie awake, haunted by the sound of my own breathing, irritated by the wheezing, frightened by the tightness... even more by the inhaler. On occasions I did resort to using it, but only when my exhaustion overcame my fear of addiction. With each cold that developed, I used it more. With each use, I felt my failure.

When it ran out, I never replaced it.

It was painfully embarrassing to have to admit this to the asthma nurse. "You mean you don't use a preventer at all?" she asked, then lifted her eyebrows and raised a dry wit.

"It never seems to make any difference," I cried, buttering denial over a thin slice of shame. "And it doesn't bother me till I get a cold."

Acknowledging this, and ignoring it completely, she asked if I'd ever done a peak flow reading... then she played a cruel trick. She produced a squared tube of plastic with a measuring gauge and a mouthpiece. "This measures how well your lungs are working," she said and presented it to my husband, asking him to blow into it. "Now you," she said and compared his result with mine.

She didn't have to speak a word to make her point. "Bring Amy back in one week," she said, trying not to be smug. "And make an appointment for yourself."

For four weeks after this appointment, I was stubborn enough to record my peak flow, determined to prove her wrong and convinced that those tiny dots on the graph, quietly rising, had nothing at all to do with the Becotide.

It was Amy who finally defeated me. With each week that passed she was sleeping better through the night and coughing less through the day. After two months, that tiny ball she curled into was gone. She's seven now and watching her race that hill, the same hill that drove my mother to her knees, is all the proof I need. I have a stubborn seven-year-old whose entire life is one vast explosion of energy. I have asthma. Only one of them causes chaos in my life.

Trudi James
⌘
A Battle Against Prejudice

Abbi May looked up at her strong, loving husband her own heart so full of love and admiration she thought it would burst. Never had she been so happy, contented and, well, never had she had so much. She looked around their home full of pride at what they had achieved together. They had done so much in six short years. Matt and Abbi had gone from living together in a flat to getting married, buying a car and a home. Matt had done most of the work himself and Abbi had helped out with what she could. She couldn't believe how lucky she now was, she even had a job which she really loved and enjoyed. Abbi at last, felt that she was a whole person and that her life actually was worthwhile. But it hadn't always been like this.

For years Abbi had battled with a mental illness, a chemical imbalance that sent her into the dark depths of depression and desperation. She had struggled with it for half of her life. It had robbed her of so much, her home, her husband and even her children. Her husband couldn't understand why she didn't want to live; they had three beautiful children, what possible explanation could there be. He thought she was totally mad, off her head, lost the plot completely. So he had decided it would be best for the children if she stayed away. End of marriage, end of children. Then what memories Abbi had of the children were dissolved over the years by all the drugs she was placed on. Nobody, but nobody, tried to find out what was causing the problem. But then in those days all they did was place you on medication so that you were quiet and didn't cause any problems. Abbi had nobody to help her fight her corner, no one to say 'Hey, this isn't right.' So she went on alone in the chaos and turmoil of her darkness. She tried so hard to fight the demons that rose within her. Sometimes she'd win and get a job, life would seem okay for a while, but then the darkness would swallow her up again and she'd lose the job. She ended up in hospital on more than one occasion. In the end the doctors felt they could do nothing more to help. They felt she needed more specialised care and treatment and so, with Abbi's consent, they sent her away.

This was the turning point for Abbi May Daytona. Whilst at the treatment centre, Abbi made some life changing decisions, she decided not to go back to the area she had lived in. She knew her children were being well looked after, even though she was unable to see them, so she felt she had no reason to go back. It wasn't an easy decision and Abbi knew it would be hard, but she felt a lot stronger now, she knew in her heart that she could do this. It was the right move for her to make at this point in time.

When her time came she moved out of the treatment centre and found herself a flat. Determined to get on with her life she scouted around the town asking about work within some of the retail outlets. It only took her a week and she had the offer of three jobs. She took on two of them as they were both part time and she needed the money. Abbi was not the sort of girl to do things by halves, when she took something on she threw her heart and soul into it. If she was going to do a job then she was going to do it to the best of her ability. Unfortunately, this was to be her downfall; it all got too much for her working seven days a week. In the end she just couldn't cope with it all and reverted to her old coping methods of not eating and taking rather more than the stated dose of pain relief to ease the pain she was feeling inside. Now we all know that pain relief in whatever form, whatever the amount, will not take away the emotional pain, nor will it deal with stress or the tension of doing too much. So it wasn't long before her boss noticed that Abbi was getting more and more stressed out. In the end, because she was unable to concentrate on the job in hand she was asked to leave. That left Abbi with just the one job. Sure, she had more free time on her hands, but she also had less money. In order to deal with her job loss Abbi found herself taking more and more pain relief until in the end she collapsed at work. Once again she was admitted to hospital, but only for the weekend. She was asked to attend a clinic to be assessed on the Monday morning. Abbi was worried, even a little frightened, but she needn't have been. They were all very nice, kind people and the upshot of the meeting was for Abbi May to attend a day centre twice weekly. Seeing as Abbi couldn't drive they even arranged transport for her.

Abbi May didn't know it at the time but this became the best turning point she could ever have hoped for. You see she had a regular driver who picked her up each week and they got on great. The banter between them was easy and free flowing. Abbi found she could talk to Matt about anything and everything and often did just that. He was a lot older than she was but that didn't bother Abbi, she had never got on with people her own age as she found them to be silly and shallow. Over the months that followed they got to know each other pretty well and it wasn't long before Matt was dropping in for coffee if he had time on his hands. Gradually things progressed between them and they spent more and more time together. In the end Matt declared his love for Abbi and she admitted to feeling the same way. They had both been hurt pretty badly in the past and let down in a major way but they were willing to take a chance on each other. Because Matt loved her so much, he fought hard to get the best treatment he could for Abbi May. He even argued her case with one of the doctors treating her, as at the time Abbi was too ill to do it for herself. This in turn led them to a new doctor and a new form of treatment, one without pills or potions of any kind. He was gentle and kind and appeared to have all the time in the world to help as best he could. This was just what they needed. Matt and Abbi discussed the treatment after it was explained to them and Abbi felt she had nothing to lose and everything to gain by taking it on board. It was hard, very hard; Abbi had to change her whole way of living including the food she ate. But because she loved Matt so much and wanted to share the rest of her life with him, doing things together like other couples, she was willing to do it.

Abbi kisses Matt goodbye each morning now as she goes off to work. She's held down the job for over a year now and it's one she knows she's more than qualified to do. She's now a psychiatric nurse and helps others who have problems.

Trudi James

⌘

Love Tried And Tested

He took me on when I had nothing to offer
And boy oh boy how we both did suffer
At first I was fine, all well and good
But fell ill, in a crumpled heap I stood
Yet still he loved me more and more
Though I could do nothing to even the score
I suffered a mental illness you see
But pill after pill did nothing for me
Then we fell in love and married
And to a new doctor I was carried
My husband and he treated me with respect
They helped and encouraged me to select
A new treatment that would do me good
Just as they both knew it would
So now I've been well for over a year
Mind unmuddied, thoughts now clear
I'm able to support and help those like me
To regain their lives so they too can see
A new future, clear and bright
One for which they'll want to fight.

Tonie Ritchie was born in Aberdeen in 1923. She served in the WRNS during 1939-45; she married James and then retired in 1946. She had five children. Tonie has been lucky enough to go to Hong Kong, Malta and Gibraltar where her husband had appointments during his service with the Royal Navy. Since his death in 1990 she has occupied her time with travelling, volunteer work for the National Trust and writing short stories.

Tonie Ritchie

⌘

Alone, but not lonely

"Lord, now lettest thou thy servant depart in peace, according to thy word." I kept repeating this verse of the Nunc Dimitus, as I held my beloved husband's hand while he lay unconscious in his hospital bed.

Two years previously, he had officially retired, but had continued to work part-time for the D.S.S. He had been a surgeon in the Naval Medical Service for over thirty years when he decided to take early retirement. Then we had moved from Plymouth to Newcastle upon Tyne where he spent the next ten years with the Civil Service. Just after his sixty-fifth birthday he began to have pains in his back and legs. He continued working although at times he was barely able to walk. Eventually I lost my temper and told him that unless he made an appointment with our family doctor, I would leave. I had coped with so much for over forty years with all the drama and trauma our family had suffered and I no longer felt that I could cope with watching him in agony, continuing to push himself beyond his limits. He realised that I meant it and allowed me to phone the next day for an appointment.

He was immediately referred to a consultant and he was admitted to hospital for tests. It was as if he suddenly gave up and no longer cared. When I saw the consultant the following day he told me that Jimmy had Lymphoma and that he didn't give much hope for his recovery. His calcium level was extremely high and he became aggressive and difficult. He reduced me to tears on more than one occasion. I did most of my grieving then, spending time in the hospital chapel for comfort on my way home.

Our children rallied round and were a great tower of strength to me during his whole illness. Eventually his calcium level was under control and he began a course of chemotherapy. He came home in between treatments, but his back was still causing problems. Two biopsies had not shown what was causing all the pain and neither had various X-rays and scans.

The Lymphoma went into remission after four months of treatment, but he was still in agony with his back. The consultants decided to refer him to the Neurological Department at the General Hospital for further investigation. Three weeks later, a further biopsy revealed traces of Brucelosis and we were told he had Osteomylitis in his fourth and fifth vertebrae. Thirty years earlier he had contracted Malta Fever and had been seriously ill in the Naval hospital. He had a course of various antibiotics and he was measured for a special corset to support his back.

Six months after originally being admitted to hospital he returned home, able to walk a little and gradually gaining strength. During the next nine months he returned to doing part-time work for the Department of Health. If he had visits to make, I would drive him and afterwards we would perhaps enjoy a drink at a pub on the way home with friends.

We had had a very happy marriage with perhaps more than our fair share of trauma, which only brought us closer together. Those last few months will remain a very precious memory to me. I knew he was still a very sick man. I had to bath and dress him every day, but such was his determination that he continued doing Medical Boards until the October when he eventually became bedridden.

He returned to hospital in the following February for a further biopsy and more tests. The ambulance men were on strike at that time and our doctor came at eight-thirty to give him a morphia injection so that he could withstand the pain of being moved. He was finally taken to the hospital in a police van and although the two policemen were as careful as they knew how, he was almost unconscious on arrival.

He was only in five days when the Registrar told me that they had had to postpone the biopsy as his kidneys had begun to fail. When I saw him that evening he was drifting in and out of consciousness and as I held his hand he would take it to his lips to kiss. That night I went home very depressed, but hoping he would rally.

However, at five o'clock the following morning the phone rang. I was told that his condition had deteriorated. I immediately phoned our sons, who said they would be with me as soon as possible. One lived in London and the other in Manchester.

As I drove to the hospital in the darkness of a cold February morning I kept thinking it was a nightmare. Our life together could not be ending like this. We had met when we were seventeen and I just couldn't imagine life without him. He had been my love for so long. When I was shown into the room where he lay, he was all wired up and was peacefully unconscious. I sat down by his side and took hold of his hand. It felt warm in mine.

Our sons arrived about twelve-thirty and we sat together until two o'clock when Sister suggested that the boys take me home for an hour or so's rest. At five David answered the phone. It was Sister to say that Jimmy's condition had deteriorated further. Being rush hour it was almost six before we arrived at his bedside. Earlier, he had been peacefully unconscious, but now lay with his eyes staring and clutching and pulling at his pyjama jacket. It was a heartbreaking sight. I could see that David and Graham were very upset. The Consultant Haematologist, who over the past eighteen months we had come to know and like and trust, arrived and told us that it was only a matter of time. When I asked him, "How long?" he answered:

"He is a tough bugger. It could be hours or it could be minutes. I am sorry we couldn't do more for him. He's a brave fighter."

He realised that we were emotionally and mentally exhausted and suggested that our sons take me home. We left about seven-thirty and at eight-thirty Sister phoned to say that he had just died. I wish now that I had stayed with him, but at the time I was just praying that he would be at peace. Graham summed up all our feelings when he said, "You wouldn't let an animal suffer the way Pa did."

The boys took charge and phoned the other members of the family who duly arrived the next day. David arranged for the funeral service to take place at the Crematorium on the Friday and he and his wife sorted through all the necessary papers. Graham and his wife made beds and prepared meals. I cannot thank them enough for all the love and support they and the rest of the family gave me.

Most of my grieving had been done when Jimmy originally went into hospital eighteen months previously. Now, all I felt was a sense of relief that he was no longer suffering. Yes, I cried and yes, I felt pain at losing him. But I remembered what he had said to me before.

"If you become a Moaning Minnie I will personally give you a kick on the backside." So for his sake and for all the love and happiness he had given me for so many years I was determined that I would think positive.

The funeral service on the Friday was family only as Jimmy had stipulated. At the lunch afterwards it was as if we were celebrating his life and the end of his suffering. He would have approved.

That was more than eleven years ago. Five weeks after Jimmy's death I discovered a lump in my right breast and had to have a lumpectomy, followed by six weeks of radiotherapy. I moved back to Plymouth where I have two members of my family close by. I have also studied for A-levels and gone on various courses and holidays abroad on my own. I still miss my beloved, but when I get low I just look at his

photograph and realise that I might soon feel a
kick on my backside. So I just dust myself down and
get on with living my life and count my blessings. I
have wonderful children and their respective
spouses and six grandchildren whom I adore. I also
have lots of good friends and neighbours and feel
that I have carried out Jimmy wishes to the best of
my ability. He is still close to me.

Phoebe Rose Gosling was

born in Buxton, Derbyshire. She currently lives in Macclesfield, Cheshire and has two daughters, two stepsons and twelve grandchildren. She is a retired medical secretary. She wrote her poem 'Therapy' as a result of her mother-in-law's skin cancer, noting down her experiences and how her outlook on life changed. Rose says after going to the clinic for treatment and meeting other people her mother-in-law realised how lucky she was and finding out what they had to go through completely changed her perspective: she became less depressed and more tolerant. 'In Praise of Rainbows' was written from her own experiences after seeing a double rainbow. She has won poetry competitions for Waterstones and Women's weekly.

Phoebe Rose Gosling
⌘
Therapy

They crossed the car park, past
wide swathes of daffodils;
"I bet they look a mess,
after they've flowered", she said;

He wheeled his mother on the glassed-in
corridor and pointed out forsythia
and vivid polyanthus round the lawn;
"It must be terrible in winter,
the wind'll sweep right through
this place, it's nothin' but
a big draught trap", she said.

Her eyes took in the lofty-ceilinged ward,
the flowered wallpaper,
the smiling faces of the staff;
"It doesn't feel like 'ome - I don't
think I shall like it 'ere".

He visited and found her talking
with a friend; "She's ad' three operations -
but there's been some talk o' more;
- an' yet she keeps so cheerful - you'd
- wonder how she could!"

Her treatment done, he came to take her home;
she waved her hand and nodded at the nurse;
and smiled along the glassed-in corridor;
they crossed the car park in the bouncing rain;
"Them daffodils are nice", his mother said.

Phoebe Rose Gosling
⌘
In Praise of Rainbows

It was a little after three, a rainy
thundery September day; tired of typing,
half-hypnotised by flickering,
fluorescent screen, I turned to look through
dusty office windows;

It hung, surpassing any painted masterpiece,
a double rainbow,
arching all heaven:

I held such joy, felt so much pleasure,
I wished the world might share these precious
passing minutes;

Surely, no-one who glimpsed this glory
could think base thoughts, do evil deeds?

And, surely, pain would be soothed,
sickness would stay its hand, before these
shimmering shafts of colour?

It was a little after three,
and all my life I will remember
the rainbows.

Marlene King, M.A. is an author,

corporate executive and mental health professional who lives in the foothill forest of the U.S. Oregon Siskiyous with her husband, cockatoo, cat and a profusion of wildlife. Her inspirational stories are featured in the national best selling books, Chocolate for a Woman's Soul, Heart and Lover's Heart series. She writes "Dream Times," a regular column in Dream Network magazine and Wellspring Journal, and her freelance work has appeared in Intuition Magazine, Odds & Ends and other professional journals. When not at her keyboard creating stories, Marlene is involved in dream studies, hospice counselling, private and commercial consulting about the intuitive and creative processes of self-empowerment and she conducts seminars and workshops in corporate and clinical settings.

Marlene King

⌘

Angel Sisters, Angel Friends

As a young child, I had a practice of placing all of my dolls around the perimeter of my room before bedtime then passionately praying to God to turn one of them into a loving sister companion who would be waiting for me when I woke up. The sweet innocence of childhood allowed me to believe that this was entirely possible. My ritual intensified at Christmas, when I was sure God would give me the gift of a sister. Although that specific miracle never happened and I remained without siblings, my belief that prayers ARE answered did not waver.

A few Christmases ago, I received a memorable reminder and miraculous confirmation that the echo of my "sister prayer" had indeed been answered over half a century later. The busyness of the holidays left a burgeoning pile of Christmas cards and mail on my desk that I had yet to open and read. As I sat down one afternoon and sorted through the stacks, I saw what was obviously a letter from a friend - I recognised her business stationery. I found this odd, as I saw her often and had just recently attended a holiday function a few days earlier where we had ample time to catch up with current news and events in our lives. I laid it aside to read later, as I was sure it contained the standard Christmas 'form letter' of reflections of her year - vacations, family, career.

When clearing my desk for the last time before the big holiday, I discovered my friend's unopened letter - an ordinary and unassuming envelope whose contents would affect me forever. I opened it and saw that it was a simple two page document that began, "Greetings to my 'angel friends.'" My heart melted when it became evident as I read, that for nearly 20 years, this dear soul had been gathering and earmarking memories of me and other special people who had touched her life in miraculous ways - people who she considered to be her 'angel friends.'

The energy of her words seemed to make this special missive glow in my hands. She candidly compiled distinctive portraits from her perspective that reflected the meandering journeys and highlights of long-standing relationships. I was amazed at her acute sensitivity, and it was apparent that she possessed unique perception and observation skills that chronicled my strengths and foibles, as only a sister could! She lovingly portrayed all of her 'angel friends' with grains of honesty, humour, humility and large measures of love and gratitude.

I have read and re-read this 'from-the-heart' letter often and am invariably touched. The sister I ached for as a child did manifest that Christmas, and reminded me that I have many lifelong friends, angel sisters, who have overwhelmed and blessed me with their love, loyalty and support, as much as any biological sisters would. My friendships are rich and

golden and have companioned me with a special
bond in ways I could never have imagined in my
childhood longings.

Steve Deeley was born in Gloucester in 1961 and now lives in Swindon with his wife and two young sons. His main hobby is writing. He has been interested in writing since an early age. He has done creative writing courses locally and hopes to carry on and do more pieces in the future. His main career has been as an electronic engineer.

Steve Deeley

⌘

Budgie

"Billy? It's nearly time."

Billy looked up and nodded. He reached for the bottle of whisky and poured two small shots.

"One for luck," he muttered and downed the first.

"And one for Budgie." He drank the second and coughed as the fire started in his throat.

Pippa watched him curiously. "You do that every time."

"What?"

"Drink a second shot to Budgie."

"Yes."

"Why?"

Billy considered the empty glass. "Because she gave me some damned good advice once."

"That's it?"

"It's enough."

He was right at the end of level five when she walked in. She stood and watched him for so long that he started to feel uncomfortable, but he couldn't pay her too much attention. He'd killed fifteen Morphoids, but there were more coming. Level six was starting to look like a futile dream.

"Stop shooting at them. Shoot at the generator up on the ridge."

"What?"

She leaned forward and tapped the screen with fingers the colour of old parchment. "It's the generator that gives them their energy. Shoot it."

A Morphoid got too close while he was distracted and took his shields down by three points. One more interruption and he was going to be toast.

"Lady!"

She shrugged. "It's your funeral."

Two more Morphoids came in. He could take one or the other, but not both. Game over. He risked a quick snapshot up at the ridge. The generator vanished in a satisfactory explosion. The Morphoids stopped. A fanfare played, welcoming him to level six. Billy couldn't hit 'save game' fast enough. He had almost forgotten she was there until she spoke again.

"Well done."

"Thanks." He turned round and grinned. She was middle-aged, but framed against the summer sun she looked older, with a tired, gaunt face. She had one of those drip stand things on wheels. It squeaked when she moved. "I mean, really thanks. How did you know about...?"

"Misspent life." She grinned and held out her hand. "I'm Budgie."

"Budgie?"

"Long story."

"I'm Billy." He shook her hand. Her skin felt dry and crinkly.

"Nice to meet you Billy. What you in for?"

He grimaced and pointed to a steel rod and bolts. "Smashed my leg up."

She wrinkled her nose. "Yuck."

"Yuck," he agreed. "How about you."

"Life," she replied cheerily. "I insulted Dr. Happer. Called him a pompous old quack. Now they've imprisoned me in revenge."

Billy grinned. "You didn't!"

"I most certainly did. He deserved it. Besides which," she added. "It's true. So are they letting you out soon?"

Billy sighed. "No. They have to stretch the leg. Otherwise it'd be shorter than the other one."

Budgie nodded. "Yeah. Can't have you going through life leaning to one side, can we?"

"How about you?"

"Nah." Budgie moved across the room and dragged up one of the hideously uncomfortable plastic bucket chairs. Her drip stand trundled after her like a hesitant child. "Reckon I'm stuck here." She yawned. "Fancy a trip into town?"

Billy looked at her carefully. She didn't look mad.

"Well?" she said. "Don't tell me you like it in here."

"We can't go out!"

Budgie pulled back and stared at him in astonishment. "My God, you're right! They took away all our civil rights. You've got a bad leg, so you're obviously not allowed to enjoy yourself. Where would the world be if hospital patients started having fun? Lord, they might even start getting better by themselves, and then where would medical science be?" Budgie stood up and raised her hands. "Chaos! Insurrection! The collapse of civilisation!"

Billy stared at her in total astonishment.

"Come on, Billy. You've killed off the entire Morphoid colony. What's a trip into town?"

He shrugged, still not quite believing her. "Okay." Then his face fell. "I can't make it that far. Not on these crutches".

"So we steal a wheelchair."

He opened his mouth to say something else, then realised he didn't have anything to say.

"Okay."

"Come on then," she breezed.

Billy struggled to his feet and clumped his way across the room. Budgie just watched him, making no move to help. Billy liked that. At least she wasn't fussing. She went ahead and checked the doorway.

"It's all clear. Come on."

They weren't doing anything more than just walking along the hospital corridor together, but it felt different. It felt exciting. And anything was better than sitting in the ward with all the little kids and the painted animals on the walls.

"Hold it!" Budgie, hugging the wall, peered around the corner. "Morphoids." She opened the door nearest to her, which turned out to be ladies' loo. She started to drag Billy inside.

"I can't go in there!"

"Billy, there is only one toilet in here. You're not going to offend any sick old dear because the only sick old dear in here is me. Got it?"

He nodded.

"Then get in. Because Happer, the Butcher of Wakefield, is going to be here in about two seconds."

Billy double-timed on the crutches. Budgie swung the door shut, plunging them into darkness. Seconds later, Happer's shoes swished by on the linoleum outside.

"Now what?"

"Come on."

They limped onwards towards the main hospital entrance. Secretaries bustled past with armfuls of files. Billy felt like everyone was watching them. Then Budgie spotted a wheelchair. It was abandoned outside the x-ray suite.

"Get in," she demanded.

"But-"

Budgie rounded on him. "Enough! Billy, let me tell you something. I've been to every continent on this planet of ours. I've sheared sheep in Australia, met gorillas in Rwanda, and got buried in a rock fall in Peru. And believe me, the worst word in this whole damn world of ours is 'but'. 'But' is what people say when they turn their brains off." She licked her lips. "The strongest cages are the ones we make in our minds, Billy. You be free. Live your life, and to hell with anything else. You only get the one chance. Enjoy it."

As Billy slid onto the seat of the chair, she smiled apologetically. "Sorry. Didn't mean to lecture you. But someone has got to know, Billy; otherwise the world might just forget. Ready?"

"I guess."

"Hold on then." As Billy watched, she pulled the drip line out her wrist.

"Should you-?" Billy closed his mouth with a snap.

Budgie grinned wickedly. "You're learning, kid. It's my body, right?"

"Suppose."

"You suppose right. Hang on then, Billy the Kid."

It was really amazing. They rolled right past a group of doctors, and out of the main doors, and nobody said anything. Not a word. Budgie was in her nightie, Billy in a T-shirt and shorts. It was summer, and Billy supposed Budgie's nightie could look a bit like a summer dress, but he thought the real reason they got away with it was Budgie. She pushed him away from the hospital as if she had every right to be doing it, as if it was the most natural thing in the world. And she kept on doing it, down the avenue outside, right at the lights and down into the town.

Billy had the time of his life. They hit PC Gamer and spent a neat hour looking at games and comparing MorphoidsII against Darken. To Billy's astonishment, Budgie told him how to get through most of the levels of both.

"California," she said. "San Jose. Where most of the world's best gamers hang out. You should get over there, kid."

Billy opened his mouth to say, "I could never do that," but then closed it again. Budgie noticed and smiled. "You're getting the idea, Billy. The only limits you've got?" she tapped her temple. "They're in here."

They left the shop and headed for the music store, where Budgie regaled Billy with tales of hanging around with some sixties groups he'd never heard of until she suddenly declared that she was hungry.

"For real food, Billy. Not that anaemic junk they serve on the ward."

Billy soon found out what that meant. Burger, fries and a thick shake the size of his forearm. Not a piece of carrot in sight. When he was finished he belched quietly and wiped the juices away with the back of his hand.

"That was really great. Thanks, Budg-"

Billy stopped. Budgie was staring fixedly out of the window, at a small wedge of blue sky. There was the ghost of a smile on her face.

He touched her arm tentatively. "Budgie?"

They didn't rush. Billy knew the answer long before the paramedic pressed his fingers into Budgie's neck. He watched as they moved Budgie onto a trolley and covered her with a blanket.

"She would hate that," he said.

The paramedic knelt by his side. "You friends, then?"

Billy surprised himself. "Sort of."

"You've had a lot of people up at the hospital very worried, Billy."

"It's my life."

The paramedic looked at him sharply. "Yes it is. But a little consideration never hurt anyone."

Billy was silent for a long moment. "What did she die of?"

The paramedic stood up. His knees cracked. "Cancer. Now don't start blaming yourself," he added, seeing the look on Billy's face. "She was dying, Billy. She knew it was just a matter of time."

"Did she really do all those things she said she did?"

"That one? Oh yes. That's why they called her Budgie, apparently. She was always restless, always flying off somewhere."

"Yeah?" Billy looked thoughtful. He was silent for a long time. "Can I ask you a question?"

"Sure."

"How much is a ticket to California?"

The knock at the door was more urgent this time. "Billy? It's gone time."

"I'm coming."

Pippa rose and checked his costume. "She really got to you, didn't she?"

"I owe her everything," he said simply. He rose and opened the door, and you could hear it then: the whole building was shaking with the stamping of thousands of feet. Billy climbed the steps, collected his guitar and headset microphone, and stepped into the light.

John Nelson was born in Blackpool in 1921 and then shortly after his family moved to Heaton Chapel in Stockport, where he was brought up and went to school. He studied for the R.A.F and took entrance exams to get in. He served with them for twelve years during the war. He married in 1945 and had two sons. His hobbies were writing, including writing his own autobiography. He also enjoyed gardening, walking and researching aircraft's. Sadly he died suddenly following a liver abscess; his family has kindly allowed us to use a piece of his work in this book.

John Nelson

⌘

A Brief Encounter

I had nothing much to do so went for a walk
I ended in the park hoping perhaps with someone to talk
It had been many years since I had visited here before
It was a lovely day so I could ask for no more

An elderly gentleman sat on a lonely park bench
Hands on lap his left with his right did clench
His brown eyes looked sad and he was deep in thought
A brief moment of intense emotion I had caught

I sat down beside him in the sun's morning rays
I wondered if he was thinking of his many past days
He turned his head and I noticed his grey hair
When he spoke it was with a slight tone of despair

"It's a lovely morning and nice to be sitting here"
I thought his last words sounded a little queer
1 wondered what was really on his mind
The answer I was soon to find

"Yes" I said in a cheery and happy way
Thinking he may have lost his wife just the other day
Perhaps a chat with a stranger like I
Would cheer him up and help time pass by

I continued "The grass and trees are all so green

This park is lovely and as quiet as it's always
been"
"Yes" he answered "I often come and sit and wonder
why
When as a young man I was made to make men die"

"You see" he said, "It's not the man in the street
who wants to fight
But the politicians and those in power with
dictatorial might
It's a case of doing what you are told for your
Country's sake
When you are young, you don't see what's in its
wake"

He continued, "In days since passed, I flew in the
air
Hunting enemy submarines, excitement indeed
beyond compare
The U boat was a terror and sank many ships
The aim to stop our supplies and food passing our
lips"

Out poured the words from the old man's mouth
"We were out on patrol over Biscay, heading south
When one of the crew shouted Sub on surface dead
ahead
Then action stations as into a dive our pilot us led

Down we went with bomb doors open wide With the
Sub on the surface it could not hide
The anti aircraft crew were in action and sending up
flak with some of the shells hitting us with a
terrifying crack

The submarine was straddled with depth charges four
They exploded lifting the stern and in water did pour
We all cheered, were excited for a U-boat we had
bent the result, time and its position in a signal to
base was sent

We were young and when in a war the enemy you
hate It's only as you grow old you think of the
others' fate You see I was the bomb aimer and the
button I did push Which sank that Sub and fifty
young men's lives did crush

At the time it never entered my head
That they were like us, someone's sons, but dead
Maybe they were ex teachers, butchers, engineers
or even a college Don
Young married men with family, now all gone

I sit here quite often and my mind wanders away
I think of the lives of those men, if they had lived till
today
Would they, like I, think of the past
Of all the havoc our efforts had cast

Both them and I just did as we were told
For me a happy life and family did unfold
But no one can realise my inner hurt
Due to the power of death with which I was made to
flirt"
He then paused, then said "I'm sorry if I have bored
you so
But I don't expect you are old enough to know
Of days of fear and war, I hope you never will
Try to love your neighbour and never kill"

He rose from the bench and with a nod
Turned and slowly the crunchy gravel trod
As he disappeared from sight and from my stare
I wondered how under a similar situation I would fare

I rose from the bench and made my way
I had said very little but perhaps had helped his day
For I had listened and not made a remark
It was still sunny and peaceful in the park

Perhaps he had wanted to get it off his chest
Maybe it had worried him and he thought it best
To explain his feelings, why I'll never know
Nor why to the park that day I should go

Elaine Marie Brown was diagnosed with breast cancer in 1992 and had a mastectomy. Six years later in 1998 she found a lump in her neck - the cancer had returned. She received radiotherapy and chemotherapy but the cancer had spread to her lungs. In January 2000, she was told the cancer had spread to her brain. Sadly Elaine lost her battle against cancer at the age of fifty. This poem highlights Elaine's great strength, optimism, bravery and the importance of her family's support. I would like to thank her husband David and family who kindly agreed to allow us to include this heart felt piece in the collection.

Elaine Marie Brown

⌘

Elaine Marie Brown

It was in 1992
I went to see the Doc
Please tell me Dr. Turner
What is this lump I've got?

He felt the lump within my breast
He said 'Now don't be grim
The chances that it's cancer
Are really rather slim'.

He sent me to Doc Nicholson
At Blackburn BRI
He took the lump, he took the breast
But said I wouldn't die.

The month it was November
The cancer hadn't spread
But still it seemed to me in fear
By Springtime I'd be dead

I came home with just one breast
But still I had my life
But would my husband David
Still want me for his wife?

It was a stupid thought to have
There was no more to say
We carried on just as before
We tried to work and play

We saw our children's 21st's
We saw our Silver Day
We saw our Philip graduate
Enjoyed each and every day

We had some lovely holidays
We couldn't wait to go
America, Canaries, Spain
With good friends Geoff and Mo

And then in January 98
The nightmare came right back
The little lump just reappeared
In the left side of my neck

Oh yes the cancer reappeared
It had begun to spread
Where had it been the last six years?
I thought that it was dead.

I had radiotherapy
It didn't do enough
The cancer spread into my lungs
I really felt quite rough

I had chemotherapy
I didn't want to die
We had so many things to do
My David Brown and I

I saw in the Millennium
But then I got the pain
They told me that this hideous growth
Had got into my brain

So now I have to wait and see
What the next few weeks will give
I know I'm on a downward track
I don't expect to live

I want to say to everyone
And this comes from the soul
To Phillip, Michael and to Sam
How much I love you all

My David has been there for me
He's really stood the test
When they were giving out husbands
I got the very best.

And so it seems that fifty years
Is all I'm going to get
I would have bet on eight-five
I've really lost the bet

Cancer is the cruellest thing
You just don't have control
You try to fight, show you are brave
But it really takes it all

Some day I'm sure they'll find a cure
We've got to fight the fight
This suffering that is hell on earth
Just surely can't be right

To all my family and my friends
The last I have to say
Remember me with kindness please
Remember when you pray.

Jon Ingold was born in Manchester in 1981. He lives in Aberdeen, but is currently at university in Cambridge studying Mathematics. He has always been a keen writer, with one publication in the Oxbridge May Anthology 2001 and has recently finished the first draft of a novel. He has also written several pieces of 'Interactive Fiction', a form of computer-based story-telling which have won various awards and commendations. Other hobbies include films and jazz music, and he aims to have a career in writing.

"Saviour" is dedicated to his mother.

Jon Ingold

⌘

Saviour

I'm not too sure when it was in my life that I became aware of him. He's been there all along, you see, a presence in the edge of my vision, a shadow around a corner, a sound just near enough to place; so that I grew up expecting a dark figure, expecting the cape and cane. There was a moment, I suppose, when I realised that this wasn't the same for everyone, when I realised it was just me with a shadow, but I don't know when that was. All I recall is a slow change, from my childhood acceptance to my youth, when I would spy for his presence, check always that he was there. Most of the time, he was not; but every now and then, often enough to keep me alert, he would light up the corner of my eye with his cloak, maybe stay, maybe slink out of sight like a cat.

I never spoke to him – at least, not for those years. I never approached him, either; perhaps somehow I responded to the innate authority that his reserved quiet demanded. I shied away from authority during my youth – I was errant, a real loser: I took my first hit at fourteen and worked my way around dealers the only way I could think, getting purer and purer stuff for my pains and my pretty little smiles. I built my life on it – I was a junkie, straight out. And I hated it, but there was nothing I could do. It was the only skill I had.

But I kept looking for him, all the same, I never tried to be rid of him and never tried to exorcise his presence. Maybe he was my reassurance, my lifeline; maybe he was just so familiar I didn't think to be afraid. I think it's just that he had always been there, so I assumed he always would be, in a strange comforting way like an old friend. He let me know I was still alive — he let me know the shadows were not empty — he let me know that someone, somewhere, would know if I came to harm. Sometimes I fantasised that he was stood in the darkness beyond the end of my bed, watching me as I slept. And maybe he was.

I do remember distinctly the first time I clearly saw his face. I was leaving a house on the nice south-side area of the city, hopping down the steps two at a time at nine in the morning. He was there, at the end of the street, stood by one of the tall ash trunks that lined the pavement, leaning on his stick like a wind-blown birch. I walked slowly toward him, walking along the road — it's quiet round the south-side all day, and nine am even more so; it's not exactly a commuter belt — till I came to a parked car. I thought I was being so cunning: I produced a lipstick, lent down and began to fix up my face, whilst examining him in the reflection of the wing mirror. I was staring at him right in the eyes — only later did I realise that of course he must have seen and allowed me to look so closely — but at the time I felt like a spy.

On his head he wore a low grey hat; I've seen them in the movies but never on anyone real before. Below the brim eyes glittered brightly, framed by grey eyebrows. He had a hawked nose, and a long and pointed chin. His Adam's apple was pronounced, just cut off by the base of the mirror.

I straightened up after way too long for just a lipstick, and turned around. But in that brief instant, of course he had gone.

He didn't start to intrude into my life until I was seventeen, and it was quite sudden. I was at a party, another crumby party, and it had got to about four in the morning — the music was low, and the bottles and cans were lying around in empty heaps, like most of the people. I was half-crashed on the carpet, Mick and Jo by my side both already gone, and I was just getting ready to join them. I'd grabbed up the needle they'd used, filled it, was rolling up a sleeve. And then there was movement behind me, and I turned, and it was him.

He took swift steps to me, and reached carefully for the syringe in my hand. Unthinking — shocked, and a little stoned — I let him take it, watching with round eyes as he produced a cork from one pocket and stabbed this neatly onto the needle-tip, before putting the whole lot carefully into a plastic bag, which he returned to his cloak.

"Dirty," he said simply.

"Who are you?" I whispered.

He looked up at me, long and hard, his eyes flickering grey and his pupils wide in the darkened room. But he said nothing more, just handed me a syringe from his back pocket; a different one, and then opened the door and left.

I stared after him, for minutes, maybe hours. The needle went unused in my hand. I found soon that I was shivering.

"Hey baby? Was it good, yeah?"
"I never did it, Mick. I was gonna, but..."
"Oh, babe. Don't tell me you chickened out! I'd never believe that!"
"No, Mick... but you'd never believe me anyway. Not this."
"What?" Jo asked, her pretty head bobbing to one side with a dim smile across it like a 'Fragile' sticker on a baby-car-seat.
"The syringe was taken from me. By a ghost, or something."
"Man!" Mick cried, leaping to his feet and waving his hands. "You let a ghost nick your drugs?!"
Jo smiled at him. I just shrugged, thinking: Yeah. I did.

Let's see. The next time he appeared I was again in the company of Mick. Yeah — there was a pause, a break for about a year when I didn't see him, and I half-missed and half got to believing it was just one of those things I'd dreamed up as a kid. And then, then he came back. I was more grateful this time.

It was after another party, though everything was in those days. Mick'd just split up with Jo; she'd kicked him out and he was touring every friend and calling in every favour in order to find somewhere to stop. I hadn't offered, but after too many drinks he was hanging on my arm, walking me home. I'd known Mick for years, but he'd become more strung out recently – he wasn't handling his break-up at all. He was going to pieces. It was more than just the woman, of course, I don't know if he even knew Jo's face from that of the postman's; but she had got him what he took, and Mick was a guy who couldn't find his own socks on the bottom of his feet for himself.

"At least you love me, Anna, don't you?" he warbled, his feet swaying in time to his breathing.
"Yeah," I giggled.
"Really love me?"
"Whatever," I replied, still smiling.
"Take me home," he grunted.
I laughed. "I can't take you home, Mick."
"Come on, baby," he whispered, leaning closer to me, his mouth by my neck. "Take me home." His voice was getting tighter, as was his grip. In a hazy drunken way I began to panic. And then shadow appeared, just in the corner of my eye, striding swiftly.

I stared, strangely detached, as that shadow came to stand just by us. It doffed its hat to me. There was a glint from under his cape as he withdrew a small silver gun. Mick barely had time to look up as it was placed onto his temple and it fired with a crack. Blood flew over the pavement like chalk-dust at school.

I didn't scream, just took a shaking step backwards, letting the body crumple to my feet. The caped man cocked his weapon once more, and slipped it into a fold of his cloak. As it lifted, I caught a glimpse of metal and wire underneath, like he was held together by it or something. I think that's why he needed his cane, because the wires went right into his skin.

"I'm sorry," he said simply. "I had to do that." His voice was that of an old man, with a faintly northern accent.

"I..." I stammered. "Why? Who are you?"

"Tell them it was another dealer."

I nodded blindly, and he turned and strode away, his cane clip-clipping along the paving stones, into the dark.

It was that time, I guess, that made me clean myself up. I told so many people that it had been gangland, just another dealer-kills-dealer, I was almost starting to believe it and I got scared. So I checked myself into rehab and spent the worst months of my life there. In all that time, I didn't see the figure, not once. Occasionally I felt he'd abandoned me, that I'd done something wrong, that this wasn't where he wanted me to be. But I went through with it all the same, and came out clean, or as clean as one can ever feel after ten years of that stuff, and I was ready to start again.

I got a job as a waitress at a cafe up in the city; took a room as a lodger with a lovely old lady who liked to make me tea and tell stories about the War. Once I got over the culture shock, that was great, and we got on fine; I told her I had just finished college and was earning some money before going to university. She treated me like the next Prime Minister. Each day she would save me the newspaper and watch as I read it. On my birthday she'd produce something useful, like a dictionary, or a calculator. She used to joke each morning: "I've had a look through the paper, Annie, but I didn't see your face today."

It was kinda down to her that I kept myself clean; I had to make all this stuff up just to keep her happy, learn so much just so as not to let her down, that I had no time for the rest of it. In a way, she became like my Mum, I suppose. As for my real Mum – well, always the way, isn't it? I've no idea where she is, and she doesn't know about me. I don't care about that, either.

Anyway. It was in that café I met Graham. He came in every day, for an hour between eleven and twelve, from the campus across the road. He was a student, though I didn't know what in – the books he read were always fiction books, story books, the kind I'd seen on my Mother's bedside table just by her purse – perhaps Graham's were trashy in a different way though, my Mother had read "Last Dance" and he read "Raiders of Time". And anyway, we got talking, somehow, about the coffee blend or the weather, and he became a regular fixture. He was shy to start with, seemed embarrassed to say what he was doing, embarrassed to be getting a degree and be looking forward to a job in a university for life. It took a while, but I got him chatting, and he proved to be a fascinating guy – so full of ideas, and thoughts, about everything. There wasn't a single subject he didn't seem to know something about.

One afternoon he finished a book in the shop, and lent it to me. I read it through, cover to cover, that evening; my landlady nothing short of beaming to see me studying for my coming English degree – I had told her History when I first moved in, but it seemed she had forgotten that, and I was careful from then on.

"What did you think?" he asked the next day, sipping his coffee, when I returned it.
"I liked it," I replied.
"Really? Why?"
"Hey?"
"What did you like about it?"

And it gave me quite a shock when I realised he actually wanted to know.

Now, for some of the time we talked together, I saw the figure. He reappeared without much fanfare one day and took to coming into the café to have a cup of Moroccan blend, just what Graham drank, and smiled quietly to himself. He never spoke to anyone, and he refused to let me serve him, having all his dealings with Ken my overseer, a fat Liverpudlian. But I caught him looking in our direction, as I sat at the table with Graham. I caught the smile of the bottom of his mouth.

And that's how I knew, I think – the shadowy man approved, so I knew to say yes when Graham asked me out for a meal one evening. It had taken him weeks to work up the courage; I had seen it coming in the extra half-hours in the café and the faltering goodbyes each day – every one as though there was something left unsaid behind his teeth. Finally he asked, simply and beautifully, if I was free. In the corner of my eye the man in the cape nodded.

"Yes, I'd love to come out," I replied.

The old man rose, collected his cane from the table, left his coins by the half-drunk cup of coffee and tapped his way out onto the street. I followed him with my eyes, and looked back to Graham.

"Hang on a second," I said to him, and hurried out in pursuit. Ken bawled at me as I left. "Ere! You errant scally!"

I caught him at the crossroads, literally — I grabbed onto a fold of his cloak, and he swung round to look at me, a little fiercely. No ghost, I thought.

"I need to know," I said, breathlessly. "Is he the one? Is that what it's about?"

The old man laughed lightly but said nothing.

"Is that why you're here?"

Smiling a lop-sided smile, his eyes twinkling, he nodded.

"Are you..." I breathed deeply, preparing myself to ask a question which had hung in my mind since my time in rehab, when I had finally thought it all through clearly. "Are you an angel? My guardian angel?"

The man laughed again, affectionately. "You could say that."

"Why me?"

He turned to glance across the street, but the lights had changed against him once more and there was nowhere for him to run to.

"I was very much in love with a woman once. She died, of AIDS, about twenty years ago. I'm here to make up for that. I worked my whole life, read every book I could, and I learnt how to do it."

"Do what?"

"You've seen me," he replied softly, waving an open hand. "There and away." He flashed a white-teeth grin in my direction, suddenly. "There's going to be a crash over there," and pointed.

"What?"

There was a squeal and a crash from up the road. I stared, two cars had just run headlong into each other, a wire of smoke reaching to the sky; and when I looked back the lights had changed and he was gone.

That evening, Graham and I went to a restaurant, a classy place on the East Side of town. Italian. I'd had Italian food before, obviously – pasta is cheap, and takeaway pizza was a staple food for years – but never this good. I was overwhelmed; Graham

seemed vaguely amused as after every course I
enthused loudly over how nice it had been.

"You don't eat out often, do you?" he asked.
"First time."
"Did your parents never take you out?"
"My Dad worked night shifts, six till six, something
like that. My Mum.... My Mum went out sometimes.
She never took us."

"Us?"
"Me or my sister, Jo."
"You never mentioned a sister before," he remarked.
"I don't often." I looked down at my lap. "She killed
herself, about half a year ago. Discovered — oh, I
don't know... she had some disease, she said. She
said she couldn't face living with it." I thought about
what the old man had said to me: "It was AIDS, I
guess. I bet it was."

"I'm sorry."
"Thank you." I shrugged. "It's okay now, though. I
guess you just get used to it."

"That's brave."

I smiled. "No-one's ever called me brave before."

We went from the restaurant to his flat; a small
place he shared with two other guys from university.
He made some tea. I poked around his room,
admiring his collection of books. There was one
shelf which I'd not seen any of before; books on
"Quantum" this and "Electric" that — he said they

were to do with his course, Physics, or Engineering, or something.

I stayed the night that night. Graham, a true gentleman, slept on the sofa.

"I've had a wonderful evening," I told him in the dark.
"So have I," came the reply, in his slightly lilting northern accent.

And I realised I was happy.

So anyway, that's how I met Graham. We stayed together, he kept me clean – hell, I don't even think of it that way anymore. I left my childhood behind, and we were a pretty ordinary couple, clean, law-abiding, all that. We got married, and lived in a little house up in Sheffield. I worked as a graphic designer, making all those patterns you get on sofas and the like, and Graham got a job at the University – Professor of Physics in the end. He was brilliant, that's what I gathered; he discovered some kind of temporal principle, though he never explained it fully, and that was okay. He was really good about that – when he came home from work, the work stopped, and the rest of the time was for the family, for me and him. I used to joke that I held him back, that if it weren't for me he'd have won a Nobel Prize or something. He said he was happier the way it was. "Besides," he said, "If I don't do it, someone else will."

And I was happy – you know, we had our arguments and everything, but yeah, basically, I was happy.

And I didn't see the caped man any more either, but then I didn't need him.

Well, that's almost true. You see, one day, I woke up, looked across the pillow and realised I was married to him.

Francis Brundish has gradually

recovered from despair to a new beginning. He was shocked and destroyed after he found his wife of thirty years had become an alcoholic. One weekend in 1977 he was visiting Coventry cathedral, when words came into his mind, which he was compelled to write down. From those words and subsequent writings he decided he might be a useful person and this was the beginning of his recovery from the depth of total despair. He later resigned as M.D of his company in Essex and took up residence in a school for sick children where he had a post as a House Parent. One year later he found he had sufficient qualifications to train as a teacher, he was then 54 but went on to teach C.D.T to disadvantaged children in other residential schools. Francis is now retired but continues his interest in woodwork and poetry as well as caring for someone with epilepsy and multiple sclerosis.

162

Francis Brundish

⌘

Crumbs

As I stood alone just before the spring;
I desired a human voice, to talk, to laugh or sing.

But there was total silence, with no cheery words.
So, I gathered up my breakfast and gave it to the
birds.

I watched, then, from my window and hoped they'd
take my gift;
So when a robin landed it gave my heart a lift.

Then all the many sparrows followed by a thrush;
Please do eat it slowly, I beg of you don't rush.

These birds were living creatures accepting from my
hand, the best I had to give them and that not very
grand.

But the fact they came and needed what I had to
give, stopped me feeling lonely and showed me
cause to live.

Jay Lee
⌘
MY STORY

You often hear about cancer touching peoples' lives
- I sometimes feel that it pretty well trampled on
mine.

First of all it took my brother who was only in his
forties. It started on the sole of his foot and worked
its way up. I will never forget going to see him in the
hospice, looking into his eyes and seeing there the
knowledge that he was dying.

Next it came to my mother. This time it was
endometrial cancer and even though she had a
hysterectomy it only bought her another couple of
years. She fought hard, had radiotherapy but at the
end said to me that she wanted to go to sleep and
not wake up. Again, something which will stay with
me forever.

My mother's death prompted me to book a well
woman check up. Events conspired to delay this,
which, now thinking back, could have been my
saving. Various appointments were cancelled
because the doctor broke her ankle, the
mammography machine broke down and then they
had problems getting the parts. Eventually, after
about four months I wrote a letter complaining and
was given the check-up free of charge.

They gave me all the relevant tests and examinations including a physical breast check which, at the time, the doctor said seemed fine. It was a couple of days later she phoned and told me that not only did the mammogram show a problem but also the cervical smear. I felt I was being targeted from both ends.

Things moved quickly after that. I saw my GP and then a specialist who gave me a needle biopsy, which confirmed that I did have cancer in my left breast. The growth was under my nipple, which was why the doctor with a physical examination and I hadn't detected it either. It also meant that I needed a mastectomy rather than a lumpectomy. The thought of the operation terrified me, but I knew that everything possible had to be done because I needed to be alive for my son who was only seven at the time. There was no way I was going to leave him without a fight.

After the operation there followed chemotherapy and then radiotherapy as well as taking Tamoxifen, the anti-breast cancer drug. It always bothers me when I read an article in a newspaper or magazine which talks about someone undergoing "gruelling" chemotherapy. This is not necessarily so. Following my first session of chemotherapy I went home and lay down waiting to start feeling ill or nauseous. After an hour I still felt fine so I got up and went about my normal routine. This was the same for the rest of the sessions and also the radiotherapy; I had my treatment and then went back to work. My oncologist had told me that it was 50/50 whether I needed chemotherapy, so it was my choice whether to go ahead or not. If I had based my decision on what I had read, I might not have had treatment which would benefit me in the long run.

At this time I saw the breast care nurse who supplied me with a prosthetic breast, but more importantly put me in touch with the local hospice. After seeing my brother in one I had always thought that these places were where people went to die. This, however, was definitely not the case at this one. As well as a wonderful lunch, you could have various treatments such as massage, manicure, relaxation, reflexology, etc., but most important was the chance to meet and talk to other people who had been through the same sort of health problems as you. Everyone seemed very upbeat and did not let things get them down.

Next in my list of operations came a cervical cone biopsy which did indicate the need for a hysterectomy. So, about a year after my first "ectomy", I had another. My ovaries were also removed as this would help to prevent a recurrence of the breast cancer.

About a year after this operation I had the first of my breast reconstruction operations. This involved an implant with a valve under the skin, which could be injected at intervals with fluid to stretch the skin and form a new breast. Next I needed my right breast reduced to match the left and, at the same time, part of the nipple was used to construct a new one for my reconstructed left breast. All this was very worthwhile because the first time I was able to wear a bikini again filled me with an amazing sense of achievement.

It has now been five years since I was first diagnosed which means I now stop taking Tamoxifen. Those years have not been easy but with the help of my husband, son and friends I do not feel they have been wasted. In fact I feel that I have been inspired to do more with my life. We took our son to Disneyland Paris and Lapland to see Santa as well as normal yearly holidays, weekends away and days out. I have joined a gym and a slimming club, now determined to lose the weight which Tamoxifen caused me to put on.

During the course of my operations and treatment I tried to visit the hospice when I wasn't at work and keep in touch with the friends I had made there. About a year ago the hospice decided that most of the people who had been going there for some time needed to "move on". Many were very upset at this so about twelve decided to form their own group. We meet once a month for lunch either at someone's house or a local pub and keep up to date with what and how we are all doing.

Sadly three have died and will be missed by us all but we know that for their sakes and ours we will continue to meet and welcome new members to carry on the group, inspiring us all to enjoy life to the full no matter what problems may befall us.

Rosemary Arthur was born in the Midlands, five miles outside of Birmingham and is now eighty-one years old. She currently lives in Worcestershire and has been a widow since 1990. She married in 1945 and it would have been her 56th wedding anniversary this year. She had breast cancer in 1966 and a mastectomy was necessary but she has had no recurrence. She has published several books and has been a keen writer for most of her life. Apart from writing, her main hobby used to be gardening which she still does with some help. She still drives which gives her plenty of independence and she also has many friends and she enjoys life very much.

Rosemary Arthur

⌘

Green memory

Green was the colour of that autumn afternoon
As we walked the Sussex Downs looking to the
Distant sea and soon cool mist encircled us
With pale green rain, soft as a gossamer veil
Gentle as a lover's sigh, shutting out the
Noisy world, helping us regain our peace and
strength to face another day.

Green were the fields in late December,
a day full of sunshine; crisp dry air-intoxicating as
rich dark wine.

A winter day as fine and green as spring on top of
the Malvern Hills with fertile acres spread to the far
horizon and Edward Elgar's spirit striding through
my head the music of the gods.

Green was the colour of the surgeon's gown green
as the pastures beside the still waters in my
voiceless recitation echoing down the memory of
years ago. The sky has never seemed so blue nor
grass so green, nor life so precious each day is born
again rejoicing green are these memories, the
colour of my life.

John Martin was born in Calcutta, India in 1923. He was the son of an English army officer. His main education was at Kettering Grammar school, where his first poem was published in the school magazine at the age of twelve. This caught the eye of the senior English master, who was the mentor of the famous H.E.Bates. He advised John to write poetry at a later age after he gained more experience. This he did from 1994 onwards after contracting Parkinson's Disease. His odes have been printed in nearly thirty anthologies including international publications and he has won a number of competitions. He was appointed a "Distinguished Member" of the International Society of Poets in 1996. Most of his poems are based on personal wartime experiences during service with the R.A.F as a wireless operator. He worked in the accountancy profession until retirement and his hobbies include collecting old cigarette cards, Aviation topics, supporting the Air training corps, the Parkinson's disease society and R.S.P.C.A.etc.

John Martin
⌘
Press On Regardless

Oh! Mr Parkinson, what shall I do?
I've got the twitch and tremble – all because of you.

I used to be an artist, my subject aviation,
Necessitating pure clean lines lacking wobbly
deviation,

But alas! My shaking hand could not any longer
depict the slick and streamlined shapes
which once sped through my brain,
so I had to think of something to activate it once
again.

But then I underwent a stroke, increasing strain and
stress,
It really was beyond a joke, but I "pressed on
regardless".

So I explored the land of odes, being not averse to
verse
And took to writing poetry, for better or for worse

And in spite of all my shakes and jerks,
Anthologies were published with many of my works.

So I say to those afflicted,
Be they mother father, sister, brother,
"If fate slams one door in your mind-Open up
another!"

Madeleine Brettingham is a

third year student from Bournemouth, studying English at King's college, Cambridge who has had previous work published in 'Stand' and 'The May Anthologies' and is currently working on a novel. She got involved with the anthology because it's enjoyable to put creativity to use for a specific and worthy purpose.

Madeleine Brettingham
⌘
Charmed

My father was the famous composer Ben Smitt Walker.

(Pause.)

Please, take your time. Most people require at least a breath to prepare their response. You can see the panic in their eyes as they snatch another tube of fizz from a timely passing tray, grapple in their pockets for another cigarette. It doesn't bother me. I'm used to it. It is them I feel sorry for (though they, of course, are in all cases numb to this fact). They do not know whether to offer their congratulations or commiserations, and this I quite understand.

To say that my father was revered in the musical community is´ probably an understatement. As a young man he was its wayward child, fuming on the conductor's stand at the Old Penny Hall, his already receding black hair sweat-plastered to his brow, his caterpillar eyebrows aggressively hunched as he struggled to break another messy deal between the untranslatable keening of inspiration and the irrevocably clunky instruments that were to be (for him, it was written) the means of its delivery.

(This, I think, is the photo that Melody ran as a centre-page spread in the run-up to the 'Modified Silence' evenings. It was taken by my father's great friend Robert Walker - no relation - whom he cultivated partly for his knack of drawing out, through the camera lens, the brooding dark-eyed dignity in my father's essentially crowded, gnome-like face.)

Then there was my father the patriarch (those biblical connotations are deliberate). The Ben Smitt Walker who appeared in the obituaries, his deeply creased jowls sympathetically lit (dear Robert again), his brown eyes aimed intently, broodingly into the distance, as if his own end was already in view. At functions, young would-be composers formed adoring cherubic clusters at a respectful distance, their admiration ensuring that his every move (the swell of his cheek as he swallowed a handful of finger food, or that barely-noticeable habit that prompted him, in moments of nervousness, to reach into his top pocket for those long-abandoned cigarettes) overflowed with the dark import of genius. They did not even dare (the poor things) to interrupt his awesome thoughts for so much as a measly introduction.

Where ambitious young composers are concerned, the significance of this cannot be underestimated. Of course, they all had work that they would have sold their souls to show him. Imagine! To have the patronage - more than that, the respect - of Ben Smitt Walker! But they could not bring themselves to make a peep. They left these functions (despondently, reluctantly, lingering shamefacedly to be eyed out the door by hurried waiting staff with homes to go to) still clutching their aborted offerings in their hands.

(Sometimes an especially perky youth would find the courage to ask me to act as a courier - "Would you mind? Only I'm the biggest admirer of your father's" - My father would respond, if he responded at all, with notes that became terser and more abrupt the older he grew. "Tough honesty" he called it. He never doubted that he possessed the authority to pass judgement. I believe he was born with the seed of his own legend already budding in his brain.)

For musical London, the name Ben Smitt Walker worked as a magic charm, bestowing something of its otherworldly authority on those whose lips it passed. And it passed many lips. I have never felt as if I truly owned my name.

Tonight, it is my name I wait for. In the musky shadowed wings of the Old Penny Hall. The cello waits on the boards beside me. Shapes crowd in the darkness. People - whispering, creaking - move in the emptiness behind. I wait.

I am better, of course. Not 100%, but I work, I function. I am mobile and in the mornings I almost feel the old energy again, the unassuming brightness in the background of my life as if, once more, the tape is running, the light is hitting film. When I agreed to the three concerts (it was Menaus who asked me, Menaus the director at the Old Penny and another of my father's strictly policed knot of long-term friends), there were noises. But then there are always noises. The simple fact is, I could not have refused The concerts were to be in memory of my father, all proceeds towards scholarships for

those sheepish young composers who'd suffered
so much at his hands in the past. Selected pieces
from the 'Modified Silence' suite as well as the
turbulent 'About the End'.

I was to play 'About the End's dignified ribbonning
centrepiece, the cellist's solo.

The melody that was made for me, that made me.
SMITT WALKER GIRL RISES TO PLAY AGAIN wrote
the Times Review. And I rose, as predicted. It could
not have been any other way.

My name. "Gayle Smitt Walker". Straight-backed, the
reassuring bulk of my cello swinging from my hand, I
walk into the light that seems to shake with the full
pelt of applause. The only other human in sight is
Claud Menaus, black suited at the forefront of the
stage, turning from a tall microphone (through which
he has been talking at the bright blank oblivion
beyond) to me, and I move towards his affectionate
smile, grasp the warm dryness of his outstretched
hand. For the moment, out there must be nothing to
me. The admirers, the reviewers, Elaina, Michael,
Robert, even my stepmother Maria, now mellowly
middle-aged and remarried to a waning painter. (Of
the family, only Serena Smitt Walker is absent. Only
my sister, who, as her PA tactfully, solicitously
informed me, "will unfortunately be unable to attend
due to a prior engagement".)

A wooden chair sits waiting centre stage. A music
stand casts its slender shadow across the whitened
floor. I sit (adjusting my skirt, carefully, taking my
time, as if I am settling myself in the privacy of my

own living room, opening a book, as if it is not I who must be opened, tuned-in, ready). I take the cello from its case. And play.

The cello solo at the heart of 'About the End' was written with a girl child in mind. It is feminine, pirouetting, dove-like (my father, always a traditionalist, despite his high-profile experimentalism). The child for whom it was written was me.

I was ten years old and being taught my bow-work by the ageing, yet still effortlessly international-league Japanese cellist Ho Kilarney (of Irish foster parents), and the solo, my father was adamant, could not be played by anyone else. When the Philharmonic's rising star broached it during the tuning period prior to a rehearsal there was no stifling my father's sweat-browed red-eared rage. It was only by virtue of Claud Menaus' fatherly tact that the young pro was able to retain his place in the orchestra at all. At this stage in his career, Smitt Walker was a mere thirty-one years old, yet already he could reduce such an academy-educated award-steeped young thing to a quivering apologetic jelly. Such was the ferocity of my father's arrogance.

The piece would simply shatter into pieces if it was touched by the hands of anyone other than his sylphen, his nymph like, his incomparable Gayle. (Now he hissed through clenched teeth what later he was to croon beatifically to his circle of admirers over pre-dinner drinks. These last words I overheard, one Thursday night, whilst negotiating the forest of dark-trousered music industry legs that had temporarily sprouted, as they were wont to do, in our drawing room. To those who knew him only through print, they are no doubt difficult to attribute to such a famously irascible man. But the truth is my father often became fond, poetic, with those he trusted would understand.)

And despite these excesses, he enforced a formidable regime. Whilst Maria marshalled Robin and Serena into the car for school each morning, I waited in the dining room, cello case hugged to my side, for Ho. Our daily practice sessions stretched to nine hours.

When the pianist Taishumi Mio embarked on his heart-bursting performance of Rachmaninov's Concerto Number 2 he is reported to have seen the auditorium darken before him and the keys of his instrument become the sole source of light.

Likewise, the music journalist William Shirm claimed until his death that the first thing jazz trombonist Ed Marconi mumbled, as he stumbled off the stage after his legendary rendition of 'When the Saints' at the Buzz Club, was: "I felt it get inside me and I knew all I had to do was let the darn thing rip." (This has since passed into legend and the title of the Shirm-penned biography *Let the Damn Thing Rip: The Marconi Story.*)

A great performance is not something that happens in retrospect, it does not take you by surprise like a witty remark or falling in love. There is a point when you realise exactly where you are: on the threshold.

There is a point when you make that step. Give yourself up. Lay yourself open. Every great musician has known that moment and even some plain unremarkable ones. Every musician knows when they are about to give one of the performances of their life.

It was too late to step back (and perhaps I should have stepped back, just a little, admitted an ice-sliver of heart-saving distance. I was convalescent after all, lacking in energy. But perhaps it was for this very reason that I could do nothing but, like a gymnast falling, come and become loose). The 'Modified Silence' solo was once described-perceptively, I think, and so my father thought - as "an unravelling". I became the centre of that unravelling.

I was the opened heart loosing itself in ribbons into the bright emptiness of all that space (and it was so empty to me then, empty as a reflection). We were blank and radiant. We were the note raw in the air. We were nothing. We were open, too open.

Because I have never forgotten the smell of him: the gin-tang, the peppermints, and the faint liver-like sweat. Because I have never forgotten the expression: the twitch of what looked like disapproval at the corner of his mouth; always the clearest indicator that I had played my best, impressed him.

Because I had never forgotten him, remembering came easy. It was in the face that I felt him first.

The lingering E sharp at the threshold of the second segment, when the muscles in my cheeks froze and tingled, and my mother-blue eyes muddied over. I knew that it was you looking out. You, who could never look disgustedly enough onto this luke-warm world, returned to glare again. I felt that disgust as the moment surged, I felt it too.

I felt my arms come unloosed, their sawing, their pirouetting, fade against the blaze of light. I felt my lap, my legs, my feet (the shoes that were so pointed, so uncomfortable) I felt them drop away from me. I felt myself retract, Father, into the decreasing space where you were not, and I could do nothing but gape, blindly, numbly, appalled.

I was cold, frost-bitten in my white shirtsleeves, too old to feel this way, the strawberry wisps I should have had cropped long ago loosed from their pins and drifting ghostlike in the Thames breeze and the night-time Thames quietness (stray cars speaking softly in the distance). There was a bench, black and frost-iced, looking out over the river and I thought: I must wait there until they all come out, and someone (someone will have to, won't they, they never let you drive - death, illness, heartbreak, it's all reparable so long as you don't drive, take a hot drink, let that age-old regime of consolation ease into action) offers to take me home. Menaus in his Mercedes, so well bred, so tactfully silent.

A car pulled up.

She was wearing a faux-fur coat. She was alone.
She met my eyes and dropped her car keys into her
handbag. I tucked my cold hands into my armpits.
"Gayle", she said.
I asked, rudely, I couldn't help it, "Where's Sophie?"
I meant her PA. Serena smiled. Furrows deepened
around her big, pretty mouth.
"She doesn't work nights. I decided I am capable of
driving myself home in the evenings after all." She
glanced at the car behind her. It was deep blue,
new, something expensive. Then she glanced back
at me with narrowed eyes. "I cut my own toe nails
now, you know."

We both laughed.

'It's not over already, surely? I want to see you
play."

"You had other plans."

"Oh that," Serena cast an abstracted look over her
shoulder, along the riverbank. Those abstracted
looks, always impeccably executed. She is
conscientious, grounded. One of most oriented
women I know. Yet since childhood she has
cultivated this kind of windswept vagueness, this
airy glamour. It's visible in the worn bagginess of
her faux-fur coat, the tousle of her highlighted hair.
 "It was over in five minutes. One of the idiot
producers lost his filofax and he's now running two
days behind schedule whilst his PA reconstructs his
life for him. Which of course means the rest of us
are screwed - What time are you on?"

"I've been on. I'm finished."

"And?"

I shrugged. The eldest by eighteen months, but it was always her, with her forthrightness, that rendered me small, inarticulate. "The end."

"Well". She flipped the keys from her handbag and, with a discreet bleep, operated the waiting car's automatic locking system. "You can come for a drink then can't you."

We were whizzing towards London Bridge, and I was feeling bold. "I walked out," I said.

She shot me a look.

"I don't know why. I don't want to talk about it."

We carried on staring ahead, both of us. I couldn't stop myself from smiling. We just sat there smiling into the windscreen (I could tell Serena was smiling too, I could feel it). We were on the bridge now, and stretched out to our left the depths of the wide black water were busy with moving light. We both began speaking at once.

I was trying to explain myself, Serena was saying, "Well you know what I think of that shit...," meaning You-Know-Who.

"Don't," I said.

And she did something she didn't usually do: she finished the subject. We filtered into the next lane and Serena pointed a gloved finger at the cassette box by my knee. I opened it: Joplin, John Lee Hooker, Holiday, Dylan. Serena's world, always exotic to me.

"You know you'll never hear the end of this."

"I know," I said. "SMITT WALKER GIRL'S STAGE TERROR."

Serena gave a stretched grin. "So you're a girl again?"

"In that world I'll be a girl until they bury me."

For a second, I thought I saw Menaus' navy Mercedes slide sleekly past my window. I jumped. But if it was Menaus, he did not see me. The traffic slowed as it prepared to merge into the surge of King William Street. The North Bank glittered ahead of us close enough to touch.

P.L Holroyd was born in Manchester in 1956, and moved to Stockport where he lives currently. He has two sons aged ten and thirteen-years-old. He has had Gorlin syndrome, which makes him more prone to skin cancer, for 21 years. Whilst waiting for the pre-med to take effect before going in for an operation he started writing. It was the first poem he had ever written and he found it helped to put his feelings down on to paper. He is now in a support group and finds it good to relate to other people in similar situations. His first meeting was in 1998 when there were only eight people there are now 150+ people at the same group. He works at Stockport Cerebral Palsy where he helps people with special needs and physical and learning disabilities to use computers. His hobbies include listening to music and photography.

P.L Holroyd

⌘

Another Visit

Well here I am again at the Christie
Just arrived and shown to my bed you see
Soon someone will come and take my history
Then the doctor will check my pulse and B.P.
Soon someone will come and take some blood
Then I'll do the crossword if I'm in the mood
This is déja vu going through the same paces
Though it's nice to see the same staff, friendly faces
Then my consultant arrives, pleasant and friendly as
can be
To let me know what she has in store for me
Down to clinical illustration, what a claim to fame
Then back to the ward and the waiting game
The rest of the day is spent filling in my time
Nil by mouth from midnight tomorrow's a different
rhyme
Next day arrives and I'm up at some unearthly hour
"Can you put your gown on Paul when you've had a
shower".
Then I'm lay on the bed and I'm squeaky clean
Awaiting my pre-med and Temazepam dreams
Time passes still waiting patiently
As I'm off to the theatre presently
The theatre trolley arrives for me all right
Off down the corridor, counting the lights
Into the anaesthetic room, "You'll just feel a
scratch."
Then you're out for the count under the staff's close
watch

After the op you soon come round
The recovery team keep you safe and sound
When they are sure you're OK, back to the ward you go
To finish off sleeping and come round nice and slow
When you've fully recovered and the nurses agree
Then it's time for a treat, an N.H.S cup of tea
As your head hits the pillow you nod off again
Joan might visit later, maybe with Ashley and Ben
When they have gone another book, crossword, or doze
Let's see what tomorrow brings, who knows!
Another day arrives, "Yes please I'll have a cup."
Then off to the bathroom with towel and shaver
Won't be long Doctors' rounds are near
They may say "Go home", that's what I want to hear
No one can deny the Christie's marvellous work
But being a regular visitor is certainly no perk
People joke, "Put your feet up, good excuse for a rest"
Come on though after eighteen years it's a real pest
Had it been a one off, that would have done for me
But as it's Gorlins, I have to return regularly
Now I understand the anguish my father endured before me
But kept it all inside so as not to worry the family
I used to say "Don't worry Dad it's not something you can see"
How wrong I was, it's the surgery people see not me
When I think of what we went through for all those years
I try to look ahead but it brings me to tears
Another twelve, eighteen months, maybe even two years
Will I finally be discharged? No, no fears.

Angela Davies was born in 1943 in St. Albans, Herts. She has been married for thirty-three years and has one daughter. Angela's family has been her strength through some difficult times and this has helped her overcome adversity. Her poetry has developed and now has a more inspirational theme as her life has taken a more positive turn. These poems reflect the freedom she felt when she took the decision to leave her job and seek contentment. Angela feels that she has learned a great deal about herself through exploring new avenues. She believes that life is for living and that you only get one chance. She tries to adopt this ethos in her daily life.

Angela R. Davies

⌘

Finality

If this is all there is,
why not live each day
as if it were our last,
no time or need to think of things
which happened in the past,
or to anticipate tomorrow.
We should weigh the impact of each word
leave no thought unspoken,
there'll be no second chance
to mend what we have broken.

Angela R. Davies
⌘
Moving On

Another door is closing,
as others have before,
behind it lying hopes and dreams,
discarded on the floor.

Looking back across the years,
it all falls into place,
a human life segmented,
confined in time and space.

Who knows what friendships might have been,
what intimacies shared,
the confidences only hints,
souls glimpsed but never bared.

Another door will open,
as others have before,
the corridors are waiting
for those who dare explore.

Angela R. Davies

⌘

The Freedom of Release

I am the bird that's learned to fly,
cutting a swathe across the sky.
I am the leaf that's left the bough,
drifting earthward, falling now.
I am the wave that breaks on shore,
the ebb and flow for evermore.
I am the blind man given sight,
all his days no longer night.
I am the dumb man without word,
suddenly his speech is heard.
I am the deaf man who can hear
the sweetest music in his ear.
I am the beggar without worth,
whose meekness will inherit earth.
I am the patient bound to die,
no longer forced to live a lie.
I am the prayer that's reached His ear,
He will save those whom I hold dear.
I am the prisoner now set free,
no longer shackled – I am ME.

Adrian Weston-Jones

⌘

Try to be Happy?
Or Happy to be Trying?

Not so very long ago, I met my future wife-to-be in London, where at that time I worked for a computer company in a support role. At one of the (semi regular) after work drink sessions I met a friend of a friend, who was eventually to be my wife. I had lived in London for around fourteen years, having originally made the trek from farther north in the country like so many before me looking for work and a chance of a better future. I must admit it wasn't easy and it took me a long while in London to settle down. I did all manner of work, whatever I could, for as much as I could get just to make ends meet, and there were more than a few days when rice with baked beans was considered a good meal!.

I always knew, even as I child, I wanted to work in IT, but the hardest thing was to get the break, the foot in the door as people call it. At that time University degrees were seen as a hindrance, not a benefit, for companies were after people at the cutting edge of technology, not the text book technology of three years previous of a science that was still being created on a daily basis. That for me was the key, the fact that by pure dint of effort it was possible for me to achieve my goal, purely on the amount of effort I put into studying the latest developments and knowing how it worked, both

204

physically and mentally. Now of course things have changed, but it is still possible to get in via the back door.

However, being covered in dust and dirt from head to foot, working on a building site that was totally illegal, in both type and safety, whilst dodging unemployment officers is hardly what most people would call getting into IT. That also applies to working in kitchens, being a porter at a hospital, innumerable bar jobs, and some other building work that owing to a dishonest boss I literally ended up paying to finish. However, IT was there in my mind with me, all the time. As I worked or knocked down a wall, all I thought about was IT. Bang goes a brick, bang goes another, and like little pieces of a puzzle, the thought of working in IT was all that kept me moving forward with my life.

Eventually one day I answered an advertisement in the paper. The advertisement was for an IT job extremely underpaid, extremely long hours and extremely stressful. But nevertheless it was a job in IT, more than that it was to be my job and it was my way in.

I started as a repair engineer, nine plus hours a day travelling by car visiting people at home and at work with computer faults, just keeping my head down, just happy to be working at what I wanted to be working in. Over time, I got noticed, headhunted by a big corporation, to build servers for them all over the country. I didn't know it at the time but it was a lot bigger change than I had ever imagined. Three and a half thousand miles a week in travelling by car for one thing, even before I arrived on site to work!. After a year or so I then ran through a few companies, contracting here, temporary there, and then made IT Manager for a small foreign TV company.

After a couple of years there, again I moved onwards and upwards, eventually bringing me to the firm where I met my future wife. My wife is Spanish, having also moved from Spain for the same reasons that I had moved originally from up north. We both liked similar things, similar ideals and had similar goals. We had a fairly short relationship before we got married, being of the London mindset that if it works well, then go for it, as you don't know what tomorrow may bring.

When we were married, we continued living in my wife's apartment, just south of London's centre at a place called Brixton. Over a glass of something or other one night, we discussed the world, its places and so forth, and eventually by some roundabout way, the idea of moving was brought up. We initially laughed it off, but somehow, once the seed had been planted, it was created in the backs of our minds, never mentioned out loud properly, but still there never the less.

At this time, house prices in London were at one of the high peaks, and we inquired with an estate agent friend as to the value of my wife's apartment. Once he had told us, we nearly hit the floor. Problem was, it was and is double edged. OK, so the flat is worth a lot of money, but what then. If you want a house with garden as we did, then obviously the price is even higher, and if we wait till the house prices drop, then the flat's price drops also, so it's still the same. We were undecided what to do. I must admit it had us in a catch twenty-two situation. Then something happened, something which caused me great pain. My brother Michael died.

He was forty-two, worked in IT for a major cereal manufacturer. He had a heart attack from work related stress. In a way, he was a carbon copy of me just ten years older. So, I then had to reappraise everything I was doing, and put it into perspective, not just with a monetary value, but in a real life value sense. No point being well paid if it means you die from it, or worrying so much that you stop living life but just become part of it.

So, my wife and I sat down, and weighed up our options, what can we do, what do we want to do, and what should we do. It was around this point the option of moving reappeared, and stayed. Before long we were sat in an aeroplane with two cats, on a one way journey from London to...Ibiza. The small island off the coast of Spain with twenty-four hour parties, mad antics, crazy drunken tourists and a whole melting pot of different ideals and aims.

However, that wasn't where we were going. We were going to a different Ibiza. An Ibiza where we go for walks on the beach alone in January followed by a picnic in a field of flowers, where we sit outside in our garden at night with our cats and invite friends around for a drink and a bite to eat. An Ibiza where my wife and I can enjoy life without suffering from the pace of life of London which is so intense at times you can almost touch it. Well, we arrived, and like most tourists found our luggage delayed. Well almost, we arrived with our luggage; it was our furniture that was delayed by three weeks or so. But we didn't mind. It was a new beginning, in a new house, with a garden, views of the sea (OK, a bit of a distance - 200m) and a borrowed mattress and a couple of plastic trays for plates and some plastic forks borrowed from the local restaurant.

Eventually our furniture arrived from the UK. What a day that was! So many boxes with so many empty holes to fill. The cats were very cautious at first, but then, smelling the familiar scents of home, quickly joined in the unpacking, shredding box lids with quick abandon searching for long lost toys, or just plain curiosity, who knows?

Then came the hunt for work, which wasn't easy, but helped by my wife's mother and family and friends. I became lucky enough to work for an English company based on the island. My Spanish at that time was nonexistent, so to say I was fortunate finding work in my field, with a company that spoke English and Spanish, and who paid me a fair rate compared to other trades, would be a huge understatement.

However, one year and a month later, I resigned. It had reached the point where there was no more I could do, and no more the company could afford to do.

I decided (rightly or wrongly is still in question) to start my own company in Ibiza in IT. It is going to be a very long hard road ahead. The new car I bought last year will have to go, as will various other bits and pieces I collected along the way. So far I have stuck in car windscreens 3000 odd advertisements, handed out god knows how many business cards and basically phoned every friend we have. I still have some 7000 advertisements left to place in letterboxes and windscreens. Up to now only one phone call asking if I teach web site design, which I don't, and more wrong numbers than my nerves can stand!

As a spin off to try to get noticed, I have started a 'gaming thing' as my wife calls it. It basically involves people bringing their PC to an event, using my cables and machines to connect to other peoples PCs and playing games between themselves.

The first event was held last weekend. For two hours I set about moving tables, laying electric cables, network cables, etc, etc... Add on to that, previously driving round the island sticking notices all over the place, and the cost of printing ads, visiting shops and schools; then of course the bar owner needed paying for the hire of the room and so forth. Not to mention a small fortune for all the cabling that was required.

The result?

Four people attended. Despondent, discouraged, fed up, you bet I was. However, one lad arrived in the morning, stayed during the first few hours and disappeared for lunch, at which point I believed that would be him gone. However, to my surprise, after lunch he reappeared, with only three hours or so left, with his PC, and he still paid the full day's price, insisting he should do so.

I am doing it again in two weeks time, again there will be probably only a few people there. But that isn't important, what is important is that I am still doing what I enjoy doing, and I am happy. Happier than when I was in London with a fat salary and an even fatter behind.

Who knows what the future will hold?

It may come to pass we return to London, or go somewhere else. But, where we are isn't important to us really. All we really want is time to be together, to spend time with our cats (we have six now, having taken four refugees in) and to enjoy life.

It isn't about trying to be happy, it is about taking what you have, and being happy trying to achieve your own goals, whatever they are. For if you do fail, then at least you can say, with a smile, "At Least I Tried".

Judith Thwaite lives in Cheshire

and has four children. As well as teaching for many years she has a variety of other jobs, from park keeper to fencing instructor. She founded and edits Patchwork, with fellow writer, Don Ayers, a poetry magazine for and by those whose lives have been affected by cancer. She has had six books published by the NPF and has also contributed to the medical textbook on pain – 'Mapping the Territory' edited by Dr Bernice Carter and published by Arnolds. She was the winner of the Whitbread volunteer Action Award for the North West. She has interests in Botany and Art and runs poetry workshops in schools for adults.

Judith Thwaite

⌘

Frontline

The word Cancer evokes a whole gaunt of emotions from us as patients as well as from our family and friends. Reactions and remarks from the people round us can range from supportive to vacuous and sometimes downright doom-laden.

After talking about this to others in our support group, I thought it might help us as patients if I verbalised our concerns. I hope that we can try to laugh off some of the more bizarre remarks knowing that others suffer from them too and perhaps friends who read this may be more sensitive and think before they open their mouths.

So if you are one of the people who keep telling us that — "you look so well. I can't believe you are ill/ have cancer." Or "I'm glad you are getting better" when we have a white blood count of 2.3 and feel terrible, your slight remarks will make us feel resentful. If we occasionally need a bit of a moan (we can't keep a smile glued on all the time) then we will feel that you think we are exaggerating and shouldn't bother you.

You have to tread carefully. Now might not be the time to regale us with details of your aching bunion or your vaginal thrush. We are not always wrapped up in ourselves but please don't expect us to shed crocodile tears for you if we are in the middle of chemo and our whole body is being assaulted by toxic chemicals.

We don't want to be told that we look like a piece of chewed string and you are wondering whether to strike us off your Christmas list now. Nor do we need stories of the woman you know who died in agony after six weeks on morphine cocktails. On the other hand miracle cures you have just read about in the paper that probably have another ten years of trials etc., before being widely marketed so it won't help us if you say to us, "they're doing such marvellous things now. I'm sure they will sort you out."

We don't want to feel a sluggard when you quote Mrs. Smith from down the street who had a lung removed three heart bypasses and half her brain excised and who now goes line dancing every Friday at the Village Hall.. Do you expect us to dozydoh down the High Street with a fixed grin as we juggle three plates?

We all know to beware of the ghoul who gets vicarious pleasure from trying to prise every gasp and burp from us so that these details can be recounted (with a little embellishment) again and again to others. None of us want to be coffee morning fodder.

What we need are people around us who are positive but not unrealistically so. Those who impart to us a balanced optimism. Those who will let us know that they will be there for us come what may, who will be at the end of a telephone even if it is 3am.

When I told my sister I was ill, she cried and said, "Judi, I love you." It was enough. She doesn't need to keep reiterating it. I know she was also hurting by the news but also that she will always be there for me. Obviously friends may not be that close but perhaps a hug and an offer of practical help, even a listening ear occasionally, will say all you want to.

Judith Thwaite

⌘

Cloth Sculpture

For my rag rug I need scraps-
Felted jumpers, outgrown frocks,
Buttons and braids, pieces of mirror.
It's a rug for a wall,

A hanging of memories.
That tie he wore for a wedding,
A shredded gym slip,
Laces from her first ballet shoes
When she plied at the Village Hall.

I remember this denim dress
Worn twice then discarded,
Strips of a long black skirt
From her gothic years

When her room was draped
With beads of jet
And she splodged my towels with
"Guaranteed not to stain"—brunette.

This hanging will be a dust collector
But it will hold mind-images
Of all the young years
When days were taken at a run
A time before wrinkles
And the Times crossword.

Judith Thwaite

⌘

Here's Looking at You

When you look at me don't flinch and turn away,
Inside this skin is the same person as before.
I cry inside when I glance mirrors every day

But I want you to help me cope – not say,
"Cover yourself, dear, don't let neighbours jaw"
When you look at me, don't flinch and turn away.

Don't walk out on me. Look at me and stay.
I once had your love, now I need it more.
I cry inside when I glance mirrors every day.

I know you're scared – admit it. It's okay.
I am too. Don't bury your head in a sandy floor
So you needn't look at me, flinch and turn away.

Steroid pills make mounting scales risqué,
My hair's dropped out – it is the Chemo Law
And I cry inside when I glance mirrors every day.

I feel useless now – just a number when they
Call me for treatment – the third or four.
When you look at me don't flinch and turn away.
I cry inside when I glance mirrors every day

Hilary Adams

was born in 1927 in Darlington, Co Durham. In 1948 she graduated from Durham University, married, and lived in Zimbabwe for five years. Returning to the UK, she and her husband settled with their five children in Congleton, Cheshire, in 1963, where she taught English for twenty-two years. In 1985 she underwent a series of operations for cancer of the colon, and made a complete recovery – she is proud of missing only six weeks of teaching! After her first husband sadly died, she eventually remarried, and to date the combined families total nine children, sixteen grandchildren, and one great-grandson. Besides helping out with this vast clan, her hobbies are reading, writing (especially poetry), quilting, theatre going and running a local walking group; she also works on the committee of the Midlands Jane Austen Society and the Congleton Talking Newspaper for the Blind.

Hilary Adams

⌘

Celebration

Now I'm an old woman I'll do as I please:
Wear what I like;
Sit up till all hours watching TV;
Slummock in bed till ten reading a novel;
Drive fast.
Startle my family — have a relationship;
Get married again.
Let my children go their own way with my blessing;
Spoil my grandchildren (Grannies' prerogative:
Power without responsibility).

Twelve years ago I had cancer;
Now I'm officially "cured" (I hope. Perhaps).
So I'll do as I please:
Gather my rosebuds while I may,
Climb every mountain,
Wear out, not rust out
(And similar clichés).

Fingers crossed, I'll say yes to the rest of my life.

Jenny Harley

⌘

There's Life After Cancer

Jenny Harley had been feeling unwell for some time. She had lost weight and had little appetite.

When her stomach began to swell her GP immediately referred her to a gynaecologist at the Norfolk and Norwich Hospital as he suspected ovarian cysts.

It was coming up to Christmas and Jenny's birthday. An exploratory operation had been booked and Jenny was now very scared and worried that it might be cancer, but eager to get it over with.

The staff at the hospital were all very concerned for her.

After the surgery came the wait for the results. Jenny's worst fears were confirmed – it was cancer.

The operation had discovered tumours the size of a baby's head in each ovary. She received this devastating news on her birthday.

It was the worst day of her life.

Jenny went home on Christmas Eve not knowing whether the cancer was primary or secondary. Her family and friends supported her over the wait into the New Year. Jenny really needed their strength and love.

A week later the news came that Jenny had Non-Hodgkins lymphoma — more generalised disease which meant it could have spread anywhere.

This news was especially devastating for Jenny, as she had lost her brother to the same disease at the age of thirty-seven. Her father had also lost his life to stomach cancer at the age of fifty-two.

Jenny determined that she would fight. She had to undergo further tests, bone marrow scans and operations.

Doctor Jennie Wimperis and her team at the Norfolk and Norwich Hospital played a huge part in her life at the time. The staff at Weybourne unit and Walsingham ward were always there for her at the end of a telephone when the chemotherapy started.

Watching her hair fall out was devastating. She even lost her eyebrows and lashes. She lost weight, felt ill from all the drugs and looked like a skeleton, but still managed to smile and say to herself "I'm not giving up".

Slowly, after six months of chemotherapy, her body started to recover. Hair reappeared on her head in August and results were looking good — there were no signs of cancer. Visits to the hospital were once a fortnight, then every month.

Now, six years later, the check-ups are only every year. It is unlikely that the cancer will return now, but if it does Jenny is determined that the fight will go on.

Jenny and her family are very grateful to everyone who helped her to get well — the consultants, doctors, nurses and especially the public in giving generously to the Big C Appeal.

She is so proud that she has beaten the disease and has a second chance at life.

Jean Warham was born in Glasgow in

1943 a few years later she moved to Liverpool were most of her family were originally from and where she finished her schooling. She had cancer in 1995, was treated until 1996 and was off work for eleven months. Whilst she was ill she joined a support group which helped her through it and she wrote for Patchwork (a publication funded by The Christie Hospital NHS Trust). Before she was ill she had been in a creative writing group called 'Bollin Valley Writers'. She felt that writing helped her to deal with her feelings and also to help other people, she is now fully recovered. She works as an accountant. The main thing that inspires her to write now is that she got through her illness when she didn't expect to and she wants to try and encourage others not to give up. She now views life differently and feels she has changed for the better. Apart from writing, she enjoys gardening, is a radio amateur and a volunteer teacher for a local radio club as well as participating in a local art group.

Jean Warham
⌘
New Life – New Joy

He spent many hours preparing tempting meals for
me.
Though not hungry, I could not refuse his gifts of
love.
I passed most of that summer reclining under the
tree
In leafy dappled sunlight, growing stronger.
Now I sip each day, like fine wine, savoured in
wonder.
I regained a life I thought was lost.
Love has deepened, for he faced a life alone,
Before retreating from the edge,
And I realised the true value of ordinary things.
Cancer has dispelled complacency, and heightened
our joy.
There is good in all things, even in the dark times.

James Plant tells his touching and truly inspiring story of the loss of his father, the finest man he ever knew, through the Eulogy and poem that he read at his Father's funeral.

When we lost my Father, Keith, I was 21 years old, and had never grieved, felt loss, or had any emotional burden to deal with that compared with that shattering day. However, having known my father, I knew that I was in actual fact a very lucky young man, not to have LOST my father but to have HAD, and been raised by such a man. I am sure that much of who I am came from his take on life, and without me realising it, he had taught me many of life's important lessons, whilst all it ever seemed we were doing in our family was enjoying life. It's not that my father was forever trying to do the right thing - he just lived a life putting others first; Family, friends and strangers alike. I felt that whilst grieving, I was also capable of looking further than the facts; of how upset my mother and brother and family were, but also how lucky I was to be part of such a close family. This gave me strength to ride through my grief, in the forms of love, pride, support, and knowing that I would have been hard-pushed to ever envy anyone's family - no matter how blessed they seemed to be. I imagine this will come across in the Eulogy that was so easy to write, and so hard to read to the sea of well-wishing faces I was confronted with at my Father's funeral - perhaps the proudest day of my life.

234

James Plant

⌘

The Finest Man I Ever Knew

To be stood here in front of so many people, who meant so much to my Father, and to whom he meant so very, very much too, makes me realise just how extraordinary a man my father was. I began this week - (the last seven days, for Thursday did not exist as a day in our shock) - stating that my Father was the nicest man I ever knew; I've now changed this. It is still true, but I feel he was the finest man I ever met. I also began the week by feeling life so unfair, and feeling unjustly robbed of a perfect Father and husband by a premature death. I've since balanced my feelings by the realisation of just how lucky Craig and I were to have had him for the twenty something years of our lives. All we have of Keith now are memories, but with those wonderful memories I can reflect on how lucky we have been; I have no memory of my Father ever being nasty to anyone or anything. I have no memory of my Father ever telling me, or anyone a lie. I have no memory of anyone getting to know my Father and disliking him - 'The Finest Man I Ever Knew'.

I'd like to share with you a few words that various friends and family said when they heard of Keith's tragic death - all of them, I expect, will reflect some part of your feelings, as they do in mine. Keith was, "Larger than life", and "A gentle giant with a very infectious laugh" - "Life has lost one of its great ambassadors". "Find the biggest churches you can, and you'll fill it", "A legend in his own lifetime, in his own right", "A piece of me has died today", and "Words are so useless, aren't they"; As I'm finding now. When we speak of a piece of us dying, we all realise that this is no sliver or shadow within us, but a Keithy-sized, barrel chested, round-bellied portion of our lives.

To look at Craig and I, one would struggle to find two more different brothers. All our lives, our Father has given encouraging and supportive hands, but never dismissive or directional hands. I have a friend finishing her accountancy degree - she now realises she does not like, or ever has liked accounting, yet was persuaded into accounting by her Father (an accountant). Not once did my Father try and push Craig and I into retail, or anything else he knew we did not want. When I consider my Father as a family man, I have seen a devoted husband to my Mother, a twenty-five year long relationship with as much love and affection as one could ever hope to find. As someone commented, we were an image of just how good family life could be. He was as much the thoughtful, caring man to my Mother, as to Craig and I, and as to all of you here who knew him.

Among my earlier memories of my Father are of spending time at Abersoch, North Wales where my parents first got to know one another, a place he loved dearly, as I know do many of you here, and spending time with the family out on the boat. Now, after attempting to stop a jewellery raid on a shop in Congleton, the Congleton Chronicle, (whose front page he graced on numerous occasions), named him a "have-a-go hero"; a name which was to stick for some time. When out in the boat, nearly every seaward voyage for some time resulted in him finding stranded windsurfers, and struggling canoeists and children in dinghies very out of their depths, and each one resulted in him towing them back to dry land. All he needed was the bottle of rum round his neck to be a true St. Bernard. But this is one example of saintly action, of which there are many.

It seemed impossible to be unaffected by my Father, as all the beautiful cards we have received (over a hundred in the first couple of posts) from supportive and caring family and friends have shown. Some that my Mum and Dad knew for the majority of their lives, some from people who spoke to them for ten minutes or so. Nobody who knew my Father did not laugh with him, and with his wonderful belly chuckle and that infamous rogue eyebrow of his. He brought a wondrous humour and wit, a strength and stability unsurpassed, and a vast supply of experience of life and knowledge to every situation. He truly was a rock. He was always there to give advice; to crack a joke (however old or bad); to tell a tale or listen to one; to never judge, but merely assess. And most of all, to be the same sorely missed, stable and superb friend to all of us, myself included. If our lives were seen as wells, filled up by what we meant to other people, then I can proudly say that my Father's would be the deepest, fullest well of any man I can think of, so pivotal was he to the lives of many of us here. We feel so robbed by the suddenness of his death, and our lack of the chance to say our goodbyes. But he knew we loved him, as we know he loved us, and who amongst us would not sacrifice our chance to say goodbye for the sure knowledge that he never suffered in passing away, and to that dying a very happy and contented man.

I imagined that these words would be the hardest I ever spoke; today the hardest of my life. But I can say these words are among the easiest I've ever written, and could write ten times as many words of praise and love for this man. Now, in my Father's memory, I will try and put a smile on your faces (or he'd never forgive me) with a short verse, but finish this with a W.C.Fields quote and a thought. The Quote: - "It's a funny old world - A man's lucky if he gets out of it alive". And the thought: On considering how enriched and joy-filled my Father made our lives, we cannot in our grief, feel unlucky, but must feel lucky to have been profoundly blessed by the life of Keith Plant, THE FINEST MAN I EVER KNEW.

James Plant

⌘

The Fat Funny Fella Departs

So we have to face the fact that he's gone,
I see you acknowledge with a tear and a nod,
No more old stories, or words of advice,
and no more crap jokes - thank god!

He meant so much to so many here,
And most of us couldn't feel sadder,
But at least he'll never be wrinkled and grey,
And he still had control of his bladder.

Husband, Father, Brother and Son,
A great man who won't be forgot,
From scout leader to car-seller, DJ, to M.D.,
And male model (believe it or not).

Many of you here have known him longer than me,
Mum, old friends, his mother Nellie,
You've witnessed the rise of this wonderful man,
And the growth of his impressive belly.

He brought happiness to all who knew him,
At that he couldn't be topped.
And to finish with the words of Groucho Marx,
"Either he's dead, or my watch has stopped".

Dawn McGruer

⌘

Happiness

Happiness is a state of mind
A feeling that many don't find

Happiness cannot be bought
Neither is it the sort of thing that can be taught

Happiness can be achieved
But is hard to find when someone is bereaved

Happiness can come and go
But can be found in distant memories from long ago

Happiness is within our souls
And is released when we reach our goals

Happiness is not what we own
But can be felt from just not being alone

Happiness wouldn't exist without the feeling of being
sad
Because we need to know the difference between
good and bad

The End

⌘

All Good Things Must Come To An End

To obtain additional copies of

Character Building

Please call Aurora on

01625 536160

OR

visit our web site at

www.characterbuilding.info

If you are interested in writing for any forthcoming publications by Aurora please send entries to;

Dawn McGruer M IDM
Aurora
Suite 12, First Floor,
Rex Buildings,
17 Alderley Road,
Wilmslow,
Cheshire.
SK9 1HY.

Or for further details please contact me on
01625 536160 or
via e-mail: dmcgruer@aurora-marketing.com

I would also welcome your comments on this
publication - 'Character Building' so please
feel free to send in your views and comments to the
above address.

Many Thanks!

Dawn McGruer